COMMON CORE GRADE
MATH 7
WORKBOOK

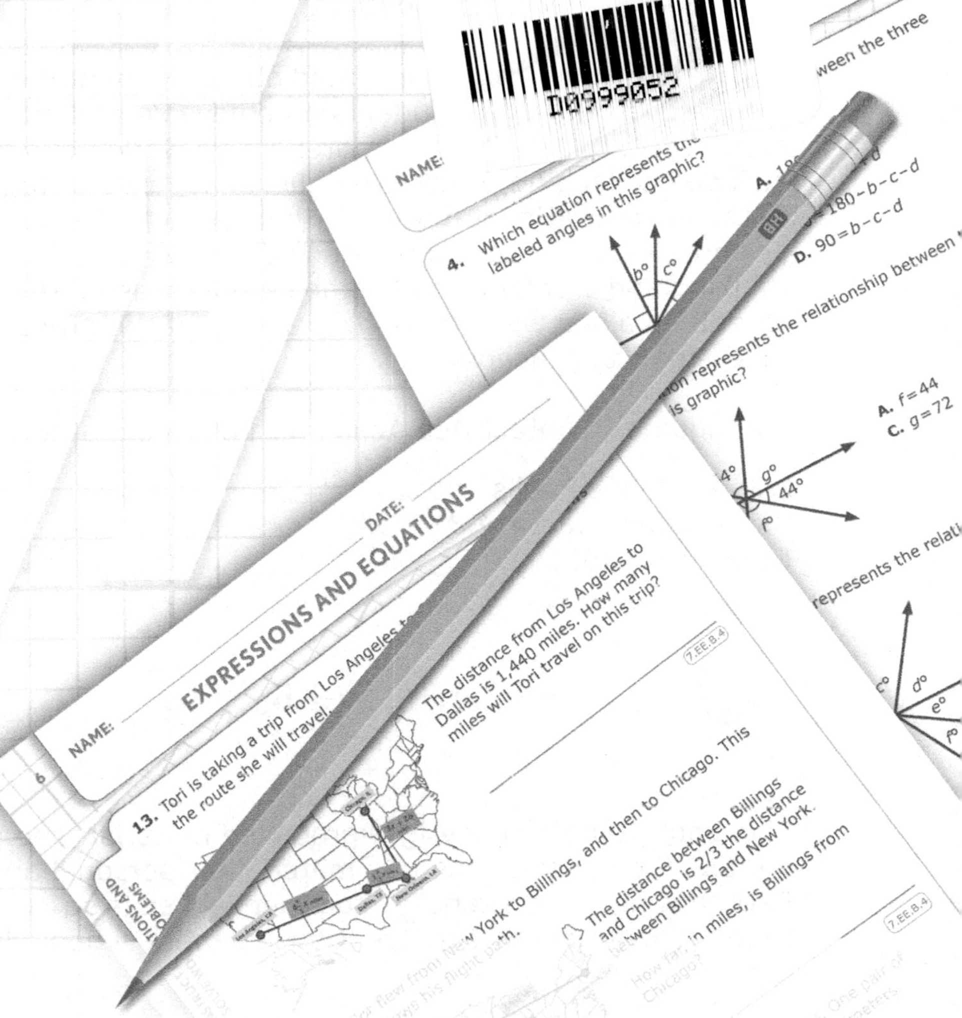

Ace Academic Publishing
ACHIEVING EXCELLENCE TOGETHER

www.aceacademicprep.com

Author: Ace Academic Publishing

Ace Academic Publishing is a leading supplemental educational provider committed to offering students an enjoyable and interactive learning experience. Through our comprehensive workbooks that are designed to include challenging, multi-step questions, we aim to provide students with state of the art educational materials that will help them improve their academic performance. Our carefully selected practice questions encourage logical thinking and creativity and combine the focus on the required common core standards along with the understanding of the practical applications of the mathematical concepts.

For inquiries, contact Ace Academic Publishing at the following address:

Ace Academic Publishing
3736 Fallon Road #403
Dublin CA 94568

www.aceacademicprep.com

ISBN:978-1-949383-05-8

About the Book

The contents of this book includes multiple chapters and units covering all the required Common Core Standards for this grade level. Similar to a standardized exam, you can find questions of all types, including multiple choice, fill-in-the-blank, true or false, matching and free response questions. These carefully written questions aim to help students reason abstractly and quantitatively using various models, strategies, and problem-solving techniques. The detailed answer explanations in the back of the book help the students understand the topics and gain confidence in solving similar problems.

For the Parents

This workbook includes practice questions and tests that cover all the required Common Core Standards for the grade level. The book is comprised of multiple tests for each topic so that your child can have an abundant amount of tests on the same topic. The workbook is divided into chapters and units so that you can choose the topics that you want your child needs to focus on. The detailed answer explanations in the back will teach your child the right methods to solve the problems for all types of questions, including the free-response questions. After completing the tests on all the chapters, your child can take any Common Core standardized exam with confidence and can excel in it.

For additional online practice, sign up for a free account at www.aceacademicprep.com.

For the Teachers

All questions and tests included in this workbook are based on the Common Core State Standards and includes a clear label of each standard name. You can assign your students tests on a particular unit in each chapter, and can also assign a chapter review test. The book also includes two final exams which you can use towards the end of the school year to review all the topics that were covered. This workbook will help your students overcome any deficiencies in their understanding of critical concepts and will also help you identify the specific topics that your students may require additional practice. These grade-appropriate, yet challenging, questions will help your students learn to strategically use appropriate tools and excel in Common Core standardized exams.

For additional online practice, sign up for a free account at www.aceacademicprep.com.

FOR ADDITIONAL PRACTICE AND HELP, VISIT OUR WEBSITE AT WWW.ACEACADEMICPREP.COM

YOU CAN FIND MORE WORKBOOKS FOR MATH AND ENGLISH FOR ALL GRADE LEVELS

TABLE OF CONTENTS

Ratios & Proportional Relationships

UNIT RATES AND MEASUREMENTS 9
PROPORTIONAL RELATIONSHIPS 14
RATIOS AND PERCENTAGES 21
CHAPTER REVIEW 25
EXTRA PRACTICE 30

The Number System

ADD AND SUBTRACT RATIONAL NUMBERS 39
MULTIPLY AND DIVIDE RATIONAL NUMBERS 44
OPERATIONS WITH RATIONAL NUMBERS 48
CHAPTER REVIEW 53
EXTRA PRACTICE 57

Expressions and Equations

EQUIVALENT EXPRESSIONS 65
EXPRESSIONS AND EQUATIONS WORD PROBLEMS 73
CONSTRUCT EQUATIONS AND SOLVE WORD PROBLEMS 80
CHAPTER REVIEW 89
EXTRA PRACTICE 98

Geometry

DRAW AND UNDERSTAND GEOMETRIC FIGURES 109
AREA, SURFACE AREA, AND VOLUME 119
ANGLE PAIRS 128
CHAPTER REVIEW 136
EXTRA PRACTICE 143

Statistics and Probability

UNDERSTANDING RANDOM SAMPLING 153
COMPARE AND INFER TWO POPULATIONS 163
PROBABILITY MODELS 179
CHAPTER REVIEW 186
EXTRA PRACTICE 194

Comprehensive Assessment 1 205

Comprehensive Assessment 2 222

Answers and Explanations 239

RATIOS & PROPORTIONAL RELATIONSHIPS

UNIT RATES AND MEASUREMENTS 9

PROPORTIONAL RELATIONSHIPS 14

RATIOS AND PERCENTAGES 21

CHAPTER REVIEW 25

EXTRA PRACTICE 30

c
a^2
b^2
A
B
c^2
a^2+
Pythagora

1. What is a unit rate?

A. A comparison between two quantities, where one quantity is 1.
B. A comparison between two quantities, that are unrelated.
C. A comparison between two quantities, where both quantities are large.
D. A comparison between two quantities, where both quantities are small.

(7.RP.A.1)

2. Which of these is an example of a unit rate?

A. 66 miles per 3 gallons of gas
B. 4 miles per 80 minutes
C. $0.78 per 1 apple
D. 2 cups of sugar per 36 cookies

(7.RP.A.1)

3. The price of 2% milk is $5.92 for 4 gallons. What is the unit rate?

A. $2.96 per gallon
B. $6.00 per gallon
C. $1.67 per gallon
D. $1.48 per gallon

(7.RP.A.1)

4. Alicia bought $2\frac{1}{2}$ dozen donuts for $8.10. What was the cost per donut?

A. $1.00 **B.** $0.27 **C.** $0.24 **D.** $3.75

(7.RP.A.1)

5. If John bought 13 sandwiches for $78, how much would it cost for 18 sandwiches?

A. $108 **B.** $92 **C.** $81 **D.** $156

7.RP.A.1

6. Kevin ran out of chocolate milk, so he went to the grocery store to purchase some. The store had a special on the milk: 3 gallons for $9.96. What is the unit rate?

A. $3.00 **B.** $9.96 **C.** $3.32 **D.** $3.96

7.RP.A.1

7. Mr. Gray drives 348 miles in 6 hours. How many miles does Mr. Gray drive in 1 hour?

A. 60 miles **B.** 56 miles **C.** 62 miles **D.** 58 miles

7.RP.A.1

8. Jamilah is buying coconut oil and finds different prices at 3 stores: Giant is selling 30 ounces for $16.50, Target is selling 18 ounces for $8.10, and Walmart is selling 8 ounces for $4.00. Which store has the best deal?

A. Giant **B.** Target **C.** Walmart **D.** Need more information

7.RP.A.1

9. Thomas' car gets 22.4 miles per gallon of gas. How many gallons of gas does he need to drive 360 miles?

A. 15 gallons **B.** 16 gallons **C.** 17 gallons **D.** 18 gallons

7.RP.A.1

10. Maria is traveling from Westwood to Briar City. She is halfway between the two cities in $\frac{3}{4}$ of an hour. How long would it take her to go the entire distance from Westwood to Briar City?

A. $\frac{3}{4}$ hour **B.** 1 hour **C.** $1\frac{1}{2}$ hours **D.** 2 hours

(7.RP.A.1)

11. The cost of your favorite soda is $3.99 for a pack of 6 cans and $8.25 for a pack of 12 cans. Which is the better deal?

A. They cost the same. **B.** The pack of 6 cans.
C. The pack of 12 cans. **D.** You need more information.

(7.RP.A.1)

12. Joseph needs gas for his motor bike. Gas costs $2.79 per gallon and his container holds 5 gallons. How much will Joseph pay to fill his can with gas?

A. $13.95 **B.** $5.58 **C.** $17.92 **D.** $15.00

(7.RP.A.1)

13. Joanna is making waffles using a recipe that requires 2 eggs. She wants to triple the recipe. How many eggs should Joanna use?

A. 2 **B.** 4 **C.** 5 **D.** 6

(7.RP.A.1)

14. It takes $2\frac{1}{2}$ cups of sugar to make 4 dozen sugar cookies. How much flour is needed to make 120 sugar cookies?

A. 6 cups **B.** $6\frac{1}{4}$ cups **C.** $6\frac{1}{2}$ cups **D.** $5\frac{1}{2}$ cups

(7.RP.A.1)

RATIOS & PROPORTIONAL RELATIONSHIPS

15. Natalie is going to the store. She sees an option to buy a 1-gallon bottle of orange juice for $6.60 or a 1 half-gallon bottle of orange juice for $3.25. Which is the better deal?

A. Both bottles cost the same.
B. The 1 half-gallon bottle
C. The 1-gallon bottle
D. You need more information.

(7.RP.A.1)

16. Eight feet of yarn costs $10. What is the cost of 1 foot of yarn?

______

(7.RP.A.1)

17. Ivan uses $\frac{3}{4}$ gallon of paint to cover half of 1 wall. How much paint is needed to cover 4 walls?

______

(7.RP.A.1)

18. A cookie recipe requires $\frac{1}{4}$ cup of brown sugar and a half stick of butter to make 1 dozen cookies. Hoda plans to make 4 dozen cookies. How much brown sugar and butter does she need?

______

(7.RP.A.1)

19. On a family hike, the Dhingra family walked for 2 hours. If they walked $\frac{1}{2}$ mile every 15 minutes, how many miles did they walk altogether?

______

(7.RP.A.1)

20. A recipe requires 6 cups of flour and 2 cups of sugar to make 2 dozen cookies. How many cups of flour would you need to make 6 dozen cookies?

____

(7.RP.A.1)

RATIOS & PROPORTIONAL RELATIONSHIPS

1. Maya is comparing the prices of 3 brands of canned vegetables. Brand A is a 16-ounce can and costs \$0.89. Brand B is a 32-ounce can and costs \$1.75. Brand C is sold as three 16-ounce cans and costs \$2.65. Which brand is the cheapest per ounce?

A. Brand A
B. Brand B
C. Brand C
D. You need more information.

(7.RP.A.2)

2. Andrew is deciding whether to purchase Car A or Car B. He wants to buy the car that has the best mileage per gallon of gas. Car A gets 23.7 miles per gallon of gas. Car B can travel 374 miles on 17 gallons of gas. Which car has the better gas mileage?

A. Car A
B. Car B
C. They have the same mileage.
D. You need more information.

(7.RP.A.2)

3. Which relationship has the same constant of proportionality between x and y in the table?

x	3	12	15
y	9	36	45

A. $y=3x$
B. $y=\frac{1}{3}x$
C. $y=3+x$
D. $y=\frac{x}{3}$

(7.RP.A.2)

4. What is the constant of proportionality in this equation?

$$y = \frac{1}{3}x$$

A. 1
B. 3
C. $\frac{1}{3}$
D. $\frac{1}{2}$

(7.RP.A.2)

5. Which equation has a constant of proportionality equal to 2?

A. $y = \frac{1}{2}x$ **B.** $2y = x$ **C.** $2x = 2y$ **D.** $y = 2x$

(7.RP.A.2)

6. Marion charges $7 per hour for babysitting. How much money will she earn if she babysits for 2.5 hours?

A. $14 **B.** $21 **C.** $17.50 **D.** $14.50

(7.RP.A.2)

7. Which graph shows a line with a constant of proportionality between x and y of $\frac{3}{4}$?

A.

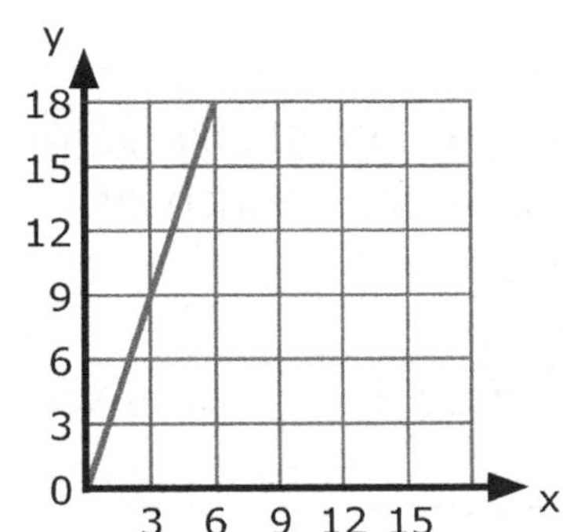

B.

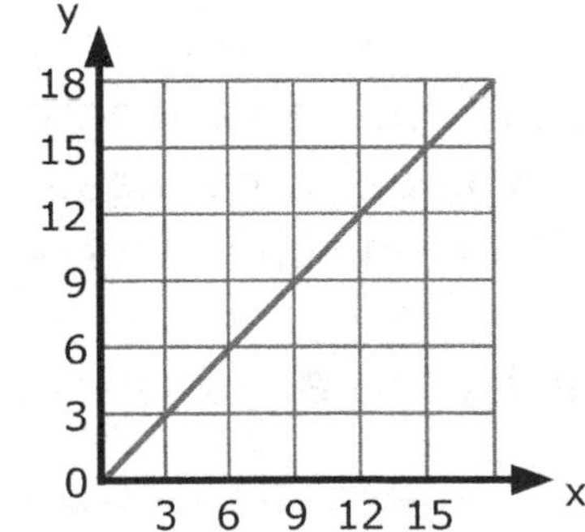

C.

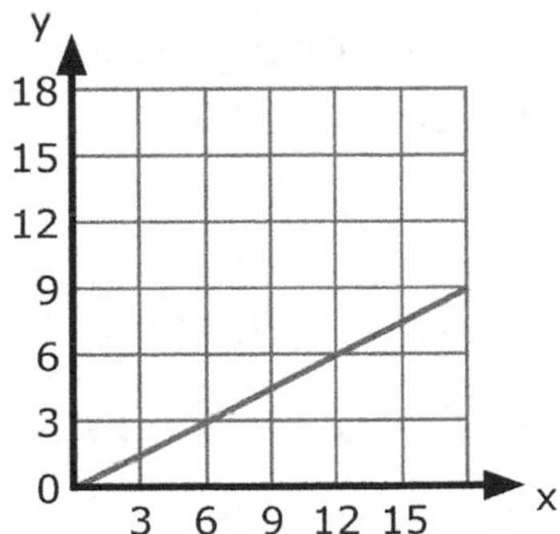

D.

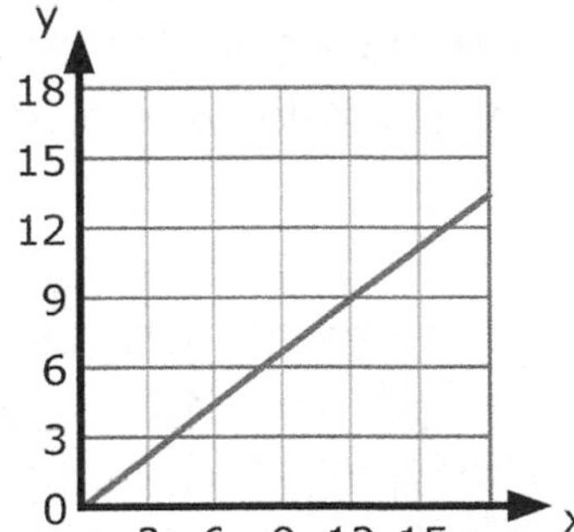

(7.RP.A.2)

8. Which table has a constant of proportionality between x and y of 3?

A.

x	1	2	3
y	30	60	90

B.

x	1	5	9
y	3	15	27

C.

x	3	6	9
y	1	2	3

D.

x	3	6	9
y	3	6	9

(7.RP.A.2)

9. Justin cut his hair to a length of $\frac{1}{4}$-inch. His hair grows $\frac{1}{8}$-inch each week. He will get it cut again when it reaches a length of 2 inches. When will Justin schedule his next haircut?

A. 14 weeks **B.** 12 weeks **C.** 10 weeks **D.** 8 weeks

(7.RP.A.2)

10. Alicia fills her pool with water at a steady rate. The relationship between the water, in gallons, and time, in minutes, is shown below. How long will it take Alicia to fill a 5,000-gallon pool?

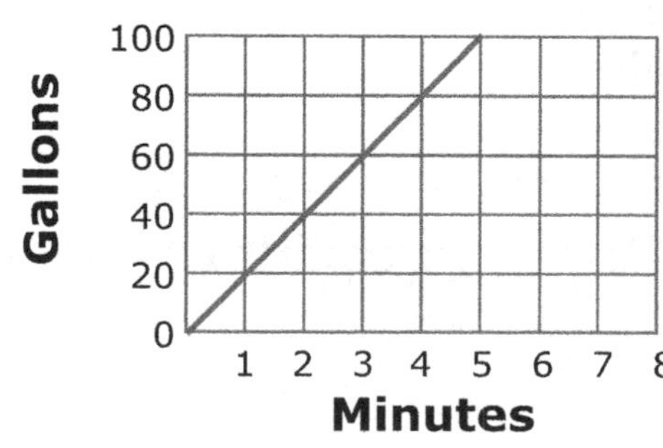

A. About 20 minutes

B. About 250 hours

C. About 4 hours

D. About 8 days

(7.RP.A.2)

11. Are the side lengths of this shape proportional?

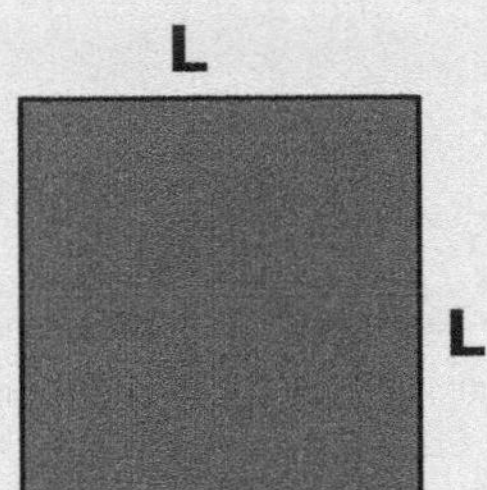

A. No, they have no numbers relating them to each other.

B. Yes, they represent a relationship of $y = x$.

C. I need more information to tell.

D. No, shapes cannot have proportional sides.

(7.RP.A.2)

12. How would you describe the following relationship between the number of children and candy bars eaten?

Children	1	3	10
Candy Bars	2	6	30

A. The number of children increases proportionally as the number of candy bars increases.

B. The number of candy bars increases proportionally as the number of children increase.

C. The number of children increases exponentially as the number of candy bars increases.

D. There is no proportional relationship between the number of children and candy bars eaten.

(7.RP.A.2)

13. Solve for y.

$$\frac{3}{25} = \frac{3}{y}$$

A. $y = 25$ **B.** $y = 3$ **C.** $y = 125$ **D.** $y = 0.12$

7.RP.A.2

14. Solve for x.

$$\frac{x}{7} = \frac{12}{28}$$

A. $x = 3$ **B.** $x = 4$ **C.** $x = 1$ **D.** $x = 0.25$

7.RP.A.2

15. The following table shows a proportional relationship between x and y. Which equation represents the same relationship?

x	2	3	4
y	8	12	16

A. $y = x + 2$ **B.** $y = 4x$ **C.** $y = \frac{1}{4}x$ **D.** $y = x + 4$

7.RP.A.2

16. This table has a constant of proportionality of 5. Fill in the table with appropriate values for y.

x	1	4	9
y			

7.RP.A.2

17. Write an equation, using x and y that has a constant of proportionality equal to 15.

(7.RP.A.2)

18. What is the constant of proportionality of the following graph?

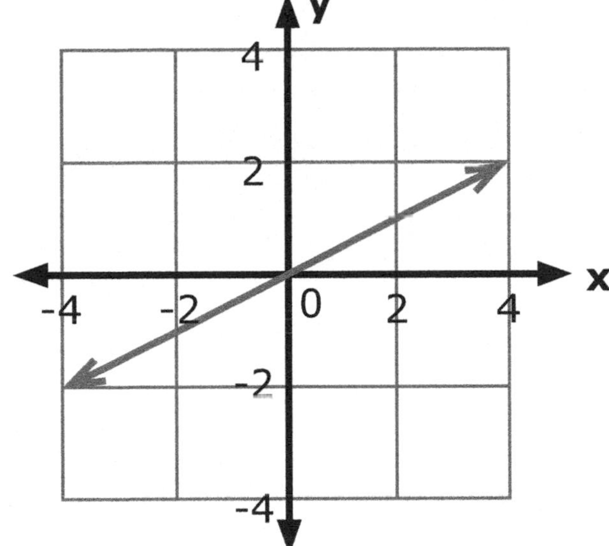

(7.RP.A.2)

19. What is the constant of proportionality of the following table?

x	4	8	10
y	1	2	2.5

(7.RP.A.2)

20. This table shows the number of pages Evie reads each hour. If she reads a 376-page book at the same rate, how many hours will it take her to read the entire book?

Time (hours)	1	2	3
Pages	32	64	96

____

(7.RP.A.2)

1. Emilio has a bank account that pays 4% interest each year. He has $200 in his bank account. How much interest will he earn in 1 year?

A. $4 **B.** $6 **C.** $8 **D.** $10

7.RP.A.3

2. Elizabeth opened a savings account with $1,500. She can earn 9% interest each year. How much interest will he earn in 1 year?

A. $100 **B.** $150 **C.** $170 **D.** $135

7.RP.A.3

3. John buys a shirt that costs $16. Sales tax is 5%. How much will the shirt cost with tax?

A. $15.75 **B.** $16.80 **C.** $17.50 **D.** $21.00

7.RP.A.3

4. Jennifer spends $20 buying music. Sales tax is 3%. What is the total price, including the tax?

A. $19.57 **B.** $18.40 **C.** $20.60 **D.** $20.57

7.RP.A.3

5. Mary spends $5 on supplies for her lemonade stand. She plans to sell each cup for $0.25. What is her profit from selling 50 cups of lemonade?

A. $5.00 **B.** $12.50 **C.** $7.50 **D.** $17.50

7.RP.A.3

6. Holiday decorations are on sale at the store for 15% off the original price. If the original price of a specific decoration Mrs. Santos wants to buy is $42, what is the discounted price?

A. $28.00 **B.** $35.70 **C.** $42.00 **D.** $57.00

7.RP.A.3

7. Which expression shows one method for calculating 12% of 56?

A. 0.12×56 B. 0.12×5.6 C. 12×56 D. 0.88×56

7.RP.A.3

8. Morgan answered 48 of 50 questions correctly on her math test. What percentage of problems did she answer correctly?

A. 48% B. 96% C. 98% D. 148%

7.RP.A.3

9. Christopher had a refrigerator delivered for $950. If he gave the delivery person a $10 tip, approximately what percentage of the sale was the tip?

A. 0.01% B. 1% C. 9% D. 10%

7.RP.A.3

10. Paul had his hair cut for $35. He wants to tip the barber 15% of the total cost. How much money should Paul give the barber as the tip?

A. $1.50 B. $5.25 C. $20 D. $37.50

7.RP.A.3

11. Last summer, the Smith family sold their house for $200,000. The realtor received 5% commission. How much money did the realtor receive?

A. $5.000 B. $10.000 C. $20.000 D. $205.000

7.RP.A.3

12. Kurt sells houses. He receives 4% of the house's final selling price as a commission. He received a commission of $4,800 for selling a house. What was the final selling price of the house?

A. $120.000 B. $124.800 C. $360.000 D. $480.000

7.RP.A.3

13. The current sixth grade class is 5% larger than last year's sixth grade class. If last year's class had 680 students, how many students are in the current class?

A. 695 **B.** 707 **C.** 714 **D.** 728

(7.RP.A.3)

14. Ed recently received a 4% raise. His yearly salary before the raise was $65,000. What is his new salary?

A. $65.400 **B.** $67.600 **C.** $69.000 **D.** $70.000

(7.RP.A.3)

15. The cell phone store is offering a 15% discount on cell phones. If the phone Wanda wants is normally $450, what is the discounted price?

A. $434.00 **B.** $449.85 **C.** $395.75 **D.** $382.50

(7.RP.A.3)

16. Lauren started her bank account with $200. After one year, she had $208 in her bank account. If she did not make any deposits or withdrawals, what was the interest rate on her bank account?

____

(7.RP.A.3)

17. Marco wanted to buy $48 worth of groceries but forgot to include sales tax in his calculations. If he has $50 and sales tax is 6%, how much more money does he need to buy all of the groceries?

____

(7.RP.A.3)

18. Jon was buying new shoes at the store. The total cost of the shoes was $70.20. If the state sales tax is 8%, how much did the shoes cost before the tax?

(7.RP.A.3)

19. Amaya wanted to buy her next Halloween costume on November 2, when the store was having a giant sale. Costumes were marked down 85%. If the original price was $49.95, what was the discounted price, to the nearest cent, of the costume?

(7.RP.A.3)

20. Mr. and Mrs. King went out to dinner. Their total bill was $84, and they would like to leave a 15% tip. How much money will they leave as a tip?

(7.RP.A.3)

1. A 12-ounce box of cereal costs $3.29. An 18-ounce box of cereal costs $4.59. Which box of cereal is the better deal?

A. The 18-ounce box
B. The 12-ounce box
C. Both boxes cost the same per ounce.
D. You need more information.

7.RP.A.1

2. Morgan needs 3 gallons of paint to paint the walls in his bedroom. If the paint he uses costs $24 per gallon, how much will he spend on paint to paint his room?

A. $24
B. $48
C. $60
D. $72

7.RP.A.1

3. Sydney saved $39 in three months. How long will it take her to save $195?

A. 5 months
B. 9 months
C. 12 months
D. 15 months

7.RP.A.1

4. Vince is buying apples for his horse. Which of these options has the lowest unit cost?

A. 5 apples for $2.50
B. 8 apples for $4.40
C. 12 apples for $7.20
D. 1 apple for $0.52

7.RP.A.1

5. Andrew travels 359 miles in his car using 13 gallons of gas. How many miles can his car go per gallon?

A. 13 miles per gallon
B. 27.6 miles per gallon
C. 26.7 miles per gallon
D. 32 miles per gallon

7.RP.A.1

CHAPTER REVIEW

6. John is making smoothies. He uses $\frac{1}{2}$ cup of orange juice and $\frac{3}{4}$ cup of fruit per serving of smoothie. He makes 8 smoothies for himself and his friends. How many cups of orange juice does John need?

(7.RP.A.1)

7. Whitney is making smoothies. She uses $4\frac{1}{2}$ cups of apple juice to make smoothies for herself and 5 friends. How many cups of apple juice is in each smoothie?

(7.RP.A.1)

8. This graph shows a proportional relationship between x and y. Which equation represents the same relationship?

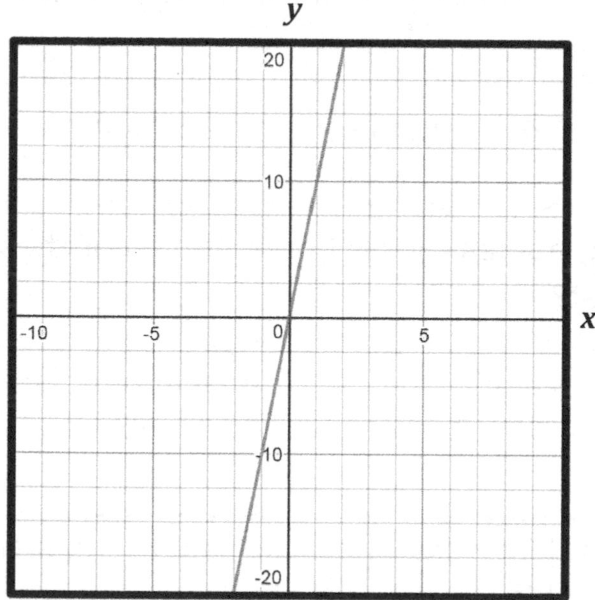

A. $y=\frac{1}{2}x$ **B.** $y=2x$ **C.** $y=4x$ **D.** $y=10x$

(7.RP.A.1)

9. Chloe jogged 3 miles in 45 minutes. Which equation represents her pace, in miles x per minute y, if she maintained a steady speed?

A. $y = 15x$ **B.** $y = 45x$ **C.** $y = x + 15$ **D.** $y = 3x$

(7.RP.A.1)

10. If 15 postcards cost $11.25, which equation determines the cost of 25 postcards?

A. $y = 25x$ **B.** $y = 0.75x$ **C.** $y = 15x$ **D.** $y = 0.45x$

(7.RP.A.1)

11. If a car can travel 368 miles on 16 gallons of gas, which equation determines how many gallons of gas are needed to travel 828 miles?

A. $\frac{16}{1} = \frac{828}{x}$ **B.** $\frac{368}{16} = \frac{x}{828}$ **C.** $\frac{368}{16} = \frac{828}{x}$ **D.** $\frac{16}{x} = \frac{828}{368}$

(7.RP.A.1)

12. This graph shows the cost of oranges per bag. What is the cost of 4 bags of oranges?

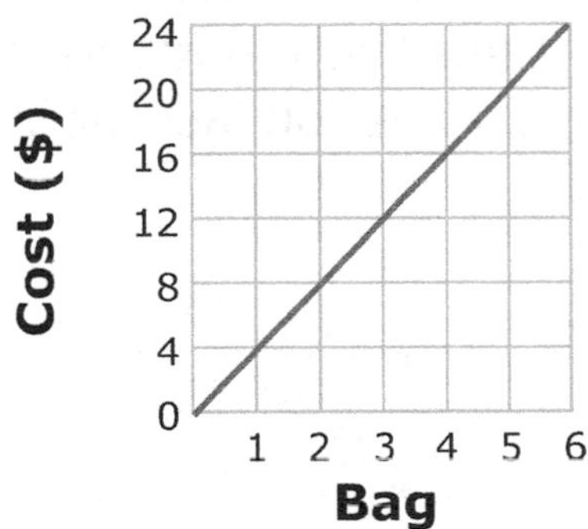

____

(7.RP.A.1)

13. Grant practices his violin for 15 minutes each night. After 8 nights, how many minutes will he have practiced the violin?

____

(7.RP.A.1)

14. Solve for x.

$$\frac{6}{4} = \frac{x}{2}$$

____

(7.RP.A.1)

15. The population of Will's town decreased 8% over a 20 year period. The population is currently 320,000. What was the population of the town 20 years ago?

A. 294,400 **B.** 304,800 **C.** 312,000 **D.** 347,800

(7.RP.A.1)

16. Mr. Robinson sells houses and receives 4% of his total sales as commission. His total sales last month were $450,000. How much money did he earn in commission last month?

____

____

____

____

(7.RP.A.1)

17. Jimmy can write 3 pages in 15 minutes. How many pages can he write in 1 hour?

(7.RP.A.1)

18. Elizabeth has a bakery. She bakes 15 cakes a day. If she must increase her production by 20%, how many cakes will she bake every day?

(7.RP.A.1)

19. In a video game, Mumia scored 24% fewer points than Shawn. Shawn scored 1,050 points. How many points did Mumia score?

(7.RP.A.1)

20. Mrs. Kim spends $120 at the grocery store every week. She spent $95 this week. By what percent, to the nearest whole percent, did her grocery bill change?

(7.RP.A.1)

EXTRA PRACTICE

RATIOS & PROPORTIONAL RELATIONSHIPS

1. Andelle packs 5 barrels of oranges every 12 minutes. Jonathan packs 4 barrels of oranges every 10 minutes. What was the difference between their packing rates in barrels per hour?

A. 25 **B.** 24 **C.** 2 **D.** 1

(7.RP.A.1)

2. A car uses 3½ gallons of gas to travel 62 miles. At this rate, how many miles can the car travel on 1 gallon of gas?

A. 631.9 miles **B.** 184.6 miles **C.** 17.7 miles **D.** 15.4 miles

(7.RP.A.1)

3. Kevin buys a gallon of orange juice for $4.35. Linda buys a 6-pack of orange juice for $3.15. Each bottle in the 6-pack contains 12 ounces of orange juice. What is the difference in the cost per ounce Kevin and Linda pay?

____

(7.RP.A.1)

4. Teresa has a cookie recipe for 2 dozen cookies. It requires $\frac{1}{2}$ cup of vegetable oil and $\frac{3}{4}$ cup of brown sugar. If Teresa wants to make 42 cookies, how many cups of brown sugar will she need?

____

(7.RP.A.1)

5. Jamal runs $\frac{1}{3}$ of a mile in 2 minutes and 20 seconds. If he runs at a constant rate, how many minutes will it take Jamal to run 5 miles?

____

(7.RP.A.1)

EXTRA PRACTICE

6. Jacki runs $\frac{3}{4}$ of the 1600-meter dash in 6 minutes and 18 seconds at a constant rate. Brea runs the 800-meter dash in 2 minutes and 30 seconds. Who runs faster? Explain why.

____

____

____

(7.RP.A.1)

7. Nat played in $\frac{7}{8}$ of the soccer games for the last two seasons. If his team had 16 games last season, and twice as many games this season, how many games did Nat play in?

____

(7.RP.A.1)

8. Carrie creates this table to represent a proportional relationship.

x	10	25	30	45	50
y	8	20	24	36	40

What equation represents this relationship?

____

(7.RP.A.2)

EXTRA PRACTICE

9. Samir believes this graph and the equation $y = \frac{1}{3}x$ represent the same proportional relationship.

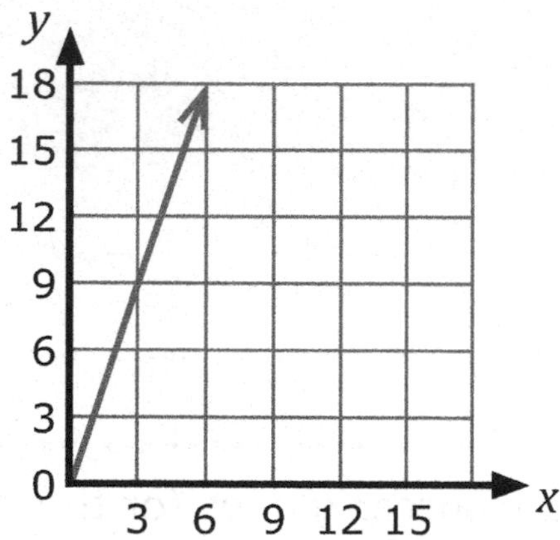

Do you agree? Explain why.

____

____

____

(7.RP.A.2)

10. What is the constant of proportionality in this equation?

$$4y = \frac{16}{4}x$$

____

(7.RP.A.2)

EXTRA PRACTICE

11. Angela uses this graph to purchase potatoes for her restaurant. How many pounds of potatoes is she able to purchase with $30?

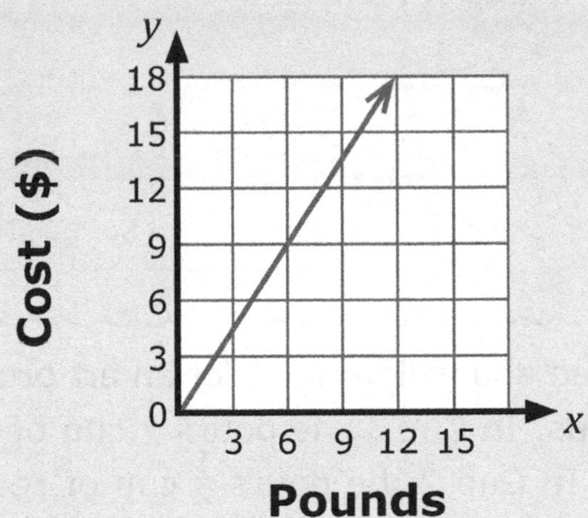

7.RP.A.2

12. This table shows the proportional relationship between the mass of a substance and its volume.

Mass (grams)	Volume (cubic centimeters)
14.83	234.31
23.72	374.78
35.44	559.95
?	662.81

If the substance has a volume of 662.81 cubic centimeters, what is the mass?

A. 102.86 grams **B.** 41.95 grams

C. 65.44 grams **D.** 12.34 grams

7.RP.A.2

EXTRA PRACTICE

13. Linda bought 5 gallons of paint for $23.95. Erica bought 4 gallons of paint for 20% less than what Linda paid for paint. Who spent more money per gallon? Explain why.

____

____

____

(7.RP.A.2)

14. Chris is mixing red and yellow paint for an art project. He mixes paint in 3 different cups. In Cup 1, he pours $\frac{1}{4}$ cup of red paint and $\frac{2}{3}$ cup of yellow paint. In Cup 2, he pours $\frac{1}{2}$ cup of red paint and $\frac{7}{8}$ cup of yellow paint. In Cup 3, he pours $\frac{1}{2}$ cup of red paint and $1\frac{1}{3}$ cup of yellow paint.

Which cups will have the same shade of paint?

____

(7.RP.A.2)

15. In 1980, there were 1,544 students at Jones High School. Between 1980 and 1998, the number of students increased by 8%. From 1998 to 2015, the number of students decreased by 2%. How many students were at Jones High School in 2015?

A. 1,451 **B.** 1,513 **C.** 1,634 **D.** 1,712

(7.RP.A.3)

16. The population of a city increases each year by 1.75%. If the population of the city is 274,000 in 2009, what was the population in 2004?

A. 250,850 **B.** 269,005 **C.** 278,795 **D.** 280,634

(7.RP.A.3)

17. Steve purchased a basketball jersey online for 35% off the original price. The original price of the basketball jersey was $95. He paid the online vendor a 7% service fee for shipping. What percentage, to the nearest whole percent, of the original price did Steve spend altogether?

____

7.RP.A.3

18. Harvey wants to buy a computer which costs $375 (including taxes and fees). He plans to put aside an equal amount of money each month for 6 months to pay for the computer.

After 3 months, the price of the computer decreased by 12%. What is the percent decrease in the amount of money Harvey needs to save for the last 3 months?

____

7.RP.A.3

19. Jocelynn paid $3.01 for an item which cost $34.80 before sales tax is applied. If the sales tax remains the same, how much money, to the nearest cent, will she pay for a $100 item?

____

7.RP.A.3

20. The cost of a pizza increased by 3.6% between this year and last year. Shaq spends $12.99 on 3 pizzas. What was the cost, to the nearest cent, of 1 pizza last year?

____

7.RP.A.3

THE NUMBER SYSTEM

ADD AND SUBTRACT RATIONAL NUMBERS	39
MULTIPLY AND DIVIDE RATIONAL NUMBERS	44
OPERATIONS WITH RATIONAL NUMBERS	48
CHAPTER REVIEW	53
EXTRA PRACTICE	57

π

3.1415926535897932384626433

1. What does $|-8+0|$ represent?

A. The value of -8.
B. The inverse value of -8.
C. The total value of -8.
D. The absolute value of -8.

7.NS.A.1

2. How do you calculate $|-16+9|$?

A. You add -16 and 9.
B. You add -16 and -9.
C. You add the values and remove the negative sign.
D. You multiply the sum by itself and to eliminate the negative sign.

7.NS.A.1

3. Which number is the value of this expression?

Increase -15 by 42.

A. -27 **B.** -57 **C.** 37 **D.** 27

7.NS.A.1

4. Which model represents $-8+5$?

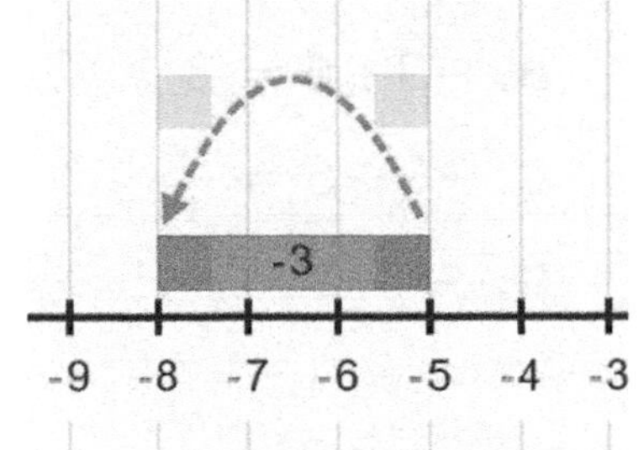

A.

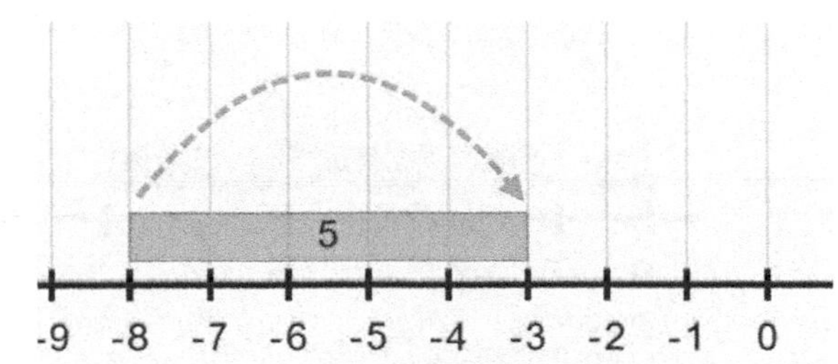

B.

C. and D. continued on next page

ADD AND SUBTRACT RATIONAL NUMBERS

C. 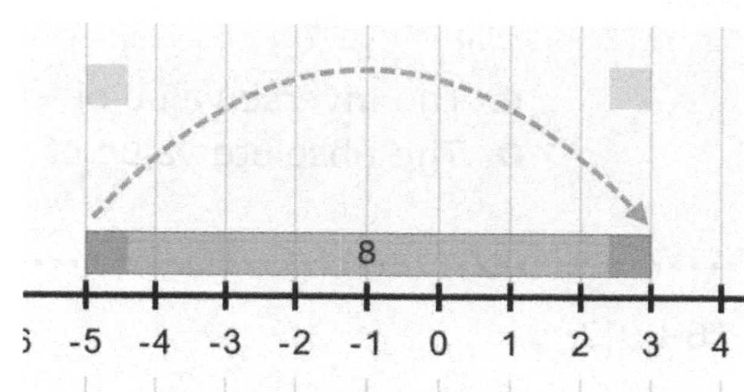

D. 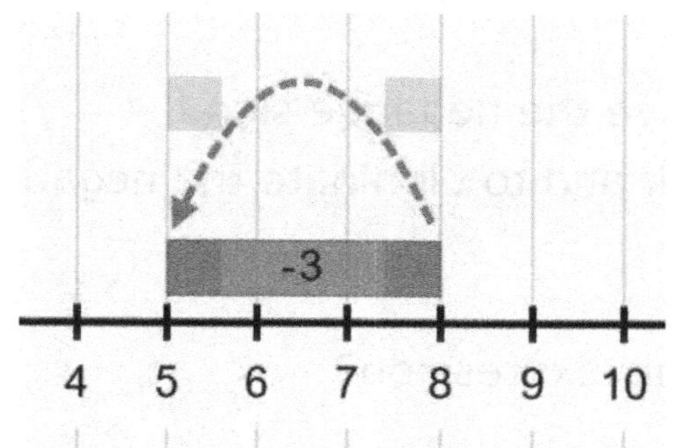

7.NS.A.1

5. Which equation is represented by this number line model?

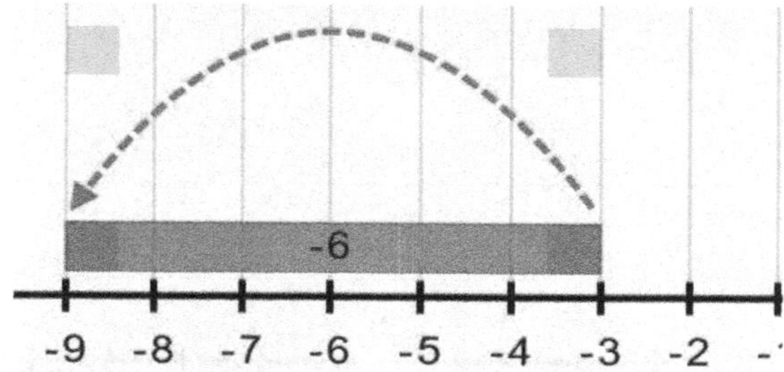

A. $-3-6=-9$

B. $-3+6=3$

C. $-9+6=-3$

D. $-6-9=-15$

7.NS.A.1

6. What is 75 minus −37?

A. 112 **B.** 38 **C.** −38 **D.** −112

7.NS.A.1

7. Which expression is equivalent to the sum of these values?

1.76 and 43%

A. $43 + 1.76$
B. $0.43 + 1.76$
C. $4.3 + 1.76$
D. $176 + 43$

7.NS.A.1

8. What is 6.547 decreased by $-2\frac{5}{8}$?

A. −3.922 **B.** −9.172 **C.** 9.172 **D.** 3.922

7.NS.A.1

9. If adding $\frac{6}{4}$ to $-\frac{1}{3}$, in which direction, from $-\frac{1}{3}$, would you move on a horizontal number line?

A. Left all the way.
B. Left to zero then right.
C. Right to zero then left.
D. Right all the way.

7.NS.A.1

10. Which value for x makes this statement true? $-11 = -6 + x$.

A. −17. **B.** 17. **C.** −5. **D.** 5.

7.NS.A.1

11. Which value of x makes this statement true? $12 = 17 + x$.

A. −5. **B.** 5. **C.** −29. **D.** 29.

7.NS.A.1

THE NUMBER SYSTEM

12. Which of the following expressions are equivalent to $-11+(-5)-2$?

A. $-11+5-2$ **B.** $-11-5-2$ **C.** $11-5-2$ **D.** $-11-5+2$

7.NS.A.1

13. Which expression has a value of -7?

A. $14-7$ **B.** $-14-7$ **C.** $-7-14$ **D.** $7-14$

7.NS.A.1

14. Which of the following is a correct interpretation of $11-15$?

A. Start at 11 on the number line and move left 15.

B. Start at number 15 on the number line and move right 11.

C. Start at -11 on the number line and move right 15.

D. Start at number -15 on the number line and move left 11.

7.NS.A.1

15. Which of the following is a correct interpretation of $-20+10$?

A. $-10-20$ **B.** $-10+20$ **C.** $20-10$ **D.** $10-20$

7.NS.A.1

16. Ed gained 7 pounds in November and 4 more pounds in December. In January he lost 15 pounds. What was his total change in weight?

A. $+4$ pounds **B.** $+18$ pounds **C.** -4 pounds **D.** -18 pounds

7.NS.A.1

17. Place the following numbers in order from least to greatest:

$$-12, |-9|, 8, |-18|, 12.$$

____

7.NS.A.1

18. The temperature today is -4 degrees Fahrenheit. Yesterday, it was 5 degrees Fahrenheit. How much warmer was yesterday than today?

7.NS.A.1

19. On a quiz, every correct question is worth 3 points and every incorrect question is valued at -1 point. If Amelia gets 6 questions correct and 3 questions incorrect, what is her final score?

7.NS.A.1

20. A parking garage, attached to a building, has levels above ground level and below ground level. If Deyan's car is 4 levels below ground level and he wants to take an elevator to level 6 of the building, how many floors will he travel?

7.NS.A.1

1. Evan is 5.9375 feet tall, Bennett is 4.75 feet tall. How many times is Evan's height than Bennet's height?

A. Not enough information **B.** 0.8 **C.** 1.25 **D.** 2.05

7.NS.A.2

2. Neil has 21 pizzas. He serves $3\frac{1}{2}$ pizzas to his family for dinner. What fraction of the pizzas is left?

A. $17\frac{1}{2}$ **B.** $\frac{5}{6}$ **C.** $\frac{1}{6}$ **D.** $\frac{1}{5}$

7.NS.A.2

3. Megan scored a 72% on her math test last week. If the test had 25 questions, how many questions did she get right?

A. 14 **B.** 16 **C.** 18 **D.** 20

7.NS.A.2

4. Which of the following expressions is undefined?

A. $\frac{8}{0}$ **B.** 0 **C.** $\frac{0}{8}$ **D.** 8

7.NS.A.2

5. Which of the following expressions is equivalent to: $-5\frac{1}{3} \div \frac{1}{2}$?

A. $\frac{16}{3} \div \frac{1}{2}$ **B.** $-\frac{16}{3} \times \frac{1}{2}$ **C.** $-\frac{16}{3} \times \frac{2}{1}$ **D.** $\frac{16}{3} \div \frac{2}{1}$

7.NS.A.2

6. Which of the following expressions is equivalent to: $-\frac{3}{8} \div -\frac{3}{4}$?

A. $\frac{3}{8} \times \frac{4}{3}$ **B.** $-\frac{3}{8} \times -\frac{4}{3}$ **C.** $\frac{3}{8} \div -\frac{4}{3}$ **D.** $-\frac{3}{8} \times -\frac{3}{4}$

7.NS.A.2

7. When dividing two positive fractions, which response describes the steps you could take first to solve the problem?

A. Find the reciprocal of both fractions and multiply.

B. You change the division to multiplication and leave the numerators the same.

C. Exchange denominators for each fraction.

D. You keep the first fraction, change dividing to multiplying by the reciprocal of the second fraction.

7.NS.A.2

8. A negative fraction divided by a negative fraction will always be ______________?

A. A positive fraction or positive whole number

B. A negative fraction or positive whole number

C. A negative fraction or negative whole number

D. A positive fraction or negative whole number

7.NS.A.2

9. Which of the following expressions is equal to: $-2 \times \frac{3}{4} \div -3$?

A. $-2 \times \frac{3}{4} \times -\frac{1}{3}$

B. $-\frac{1}{2} \div \frac{3}{4} \times -3$

C. $-2 \times \frac{4}{3} \div -\frac{1}{3}$

D. $2 \times \frac{3}{4} \div 3$

7.NS.A.2

10. What is the value of this expression?

$$(-4) \times (-4) \times (-4) \times (-4)$$

A. -64 **B.** 256 **C.** 64 **D.** -256

7.NS.A.2

MULTIPLY AND DIVIDE RATIONAL NUMBERS

11. What is the value of this expression?

$$-\frac{1}{3} \times -\frac{1}{3}$$

A. -9 **B.** $-\frac{2}{3}$ **C.** $\frac{1}{9}$ **D.** $\frac{2}{6}$

7.NS.A.2

12. When two negative integers are multiplied, the product will always be _______________.

A. Negative **B.** Zero **C.** A fraction **D.** Positive

7.NS.A.2

13. What is the quotient of a positive number divided by a negative number?

A. A large fraction **B.** A small fraction
C. A negative number **D.** A positive number

7.NS.A.2

14. When two fractions are multiplied, the numerators are _______________.

A. Added together **B.** Divided by each other
C. Multiplied by each other. **D.** Subtracted from each other.

7.NS.A.2

15. What is the product of $\frac{3}{4}$ and $12\frac{1}{3}$?

A. $\frac{4}{37}$ **B.** $\frac{37}{4}$ **C.** $\frac{18}{3}$ **D.** $\frac{8}{3}$

7.NS.A.2

16. A town's population has decreased by 320 people over the last 8 years. What was the change in town's population each year?

____

(7.NS.A.2)

17. Mike started exercising 6 weeks ago and has lost an average of $\frac{3}{4}$ pounds each week. How many pounds has he lost altogether?

____

(7.NS.A.2)

18. A bone is buried 2 feet below ground level. A dog digs $\frac{1}{2}$-foot in 30 minutes. How many hours does it take the dog to dig to the bone?

____

(7.NS.A.2)

19. Olbia make 5 withdrawals of equal amounts from her bank account. The total amount she withdraws is $680. How much money does Olbia withdraw each time?

____

(7.NS.A.2)

20. A skydiver's elevation changes by −3,800 feet in the first 4 mins after his parachute opens. What is the average change, in feet, in the sky diver's elevation each minute?

____

(7.NS.A.2)

NAME: .... DATE: ....

THE NUMBER SYSTEM

1. In Syracuse, New York, the temperature was −17 degrees Fahrenheit in the morning. If the temperature dropped 6 degrees Fahrenheit, what is the temperature now?

A. −24 degrees Fahrenheit **B.** −23 degrees Fahrenheit
C. −11 degrees Fahrenheit **D.** 11 degrees Fahrenheit

7.NS.A.3

2. In Syracuse, New York, the temperature was −6 degrees Fahrenheit in the morning. If the temperature is 14 degrees Fahrenheit now, how much did the temperature increase?

A. 14 degrees Fahrenheit **B.** 18 degrees Fahrenheit
C. 20 degrees Fahrenheit **D.** 22 degrees Fahrenheit

7.NS.A.3

3. A submarine was 950 feet below the surface. If it ascends 375 feet, at what depth is the submarine now?

A. 575 feet **B.** −375 feet **C.** 375 feet **D.** −575 feet

7.NS.A.3

4. A submarine was 250 feet below the surface. It descends to a depth of 625 feet below the surface. How far did the submarine descend?

A. 425 feet **B.** 375 feet **C.** 500 feet **D.** 875 feet

7.NS.A.3

5. An eagle is flying at an elevation of 42 feet. If the eagle soars upward 144 feet and then dives 126 feet, what is its final elevation?

A. 166 feet **B.** 60 feet **C.** 270 feet **D.** 18 feet

7.NS.A.3

6. A small airplane is flying at an elevation of 425 feet. If it ascends 63 feet and then descends 100 feet, what is its final elevation?

A. 588 ft. **B.** 402 ft. **C.** 462 ft. **D.** 388 ft.

(7.NS.A.3)

7. Jonathan was asked to simplify the following expression:

$$\frac{-7}{4} \div \frac{3}{16}$$

Which response describes the steps he will use?

A. Change the negative to a positive sign and multiply.

B. Find the reciprocal of both fractions and then multiply.

C. Multiply -7×3 and 4×16.

D. Change the division sign to a multiplication sign and multiply by the reciprocal of $\frac{3}{16}$.

(7.NS.A.3)

8. Which of these statements is always true?

A. The product of a negative number and a positive number is always negative.

B. The sum of a positive and negative number is always negative.

C. The difference between a negative number and a negative number is always positive.

D. The product of a negative number and a negative number is always negative.

(7.NS.A.3)

9. Joe wrote $|-x| = -|x|$. Is this always, sometimes or never true?

A. Never true. **B.** Always true.
C. Sometimes true. **D.** Need more information.

7.NS.A.3

10. A teacher had $487.59 in his bank account. He made a deposit of $289.56 and paid two bills of $198.67 and $323.10. What is the new balance in his account?

A. $777.15 **B.** $578.48 **C.** $255.38 **D.** $323.54

7.NS.A.3

11. Ivanka creates this timeline.

Which expression represents the amount of time that has passed between the invention of the wheel and the invention of the automobile?

A. $500 + 1886$ **B.** $(1886 + 500) - (1886)$
C. $(1886 - 500) + 500$ **D.** $1886 - 500$

7.NS.A.3

12. Paul was born in 1994 and Enza was born in 1971. How much older, in years, is Ezra than Paul?

____

7.NS.A.3

13. A scuba diver's depth changes by −75 feet in 3 minutes. What is the average change in the diver's depth each minute?

A. 150 feet/minute
B. −150 feet/minute
C. 25 feet/minute
D. −25 feet/minute

7.NS.A.3

14. The value of a car decreased by $1,750 each year for 5 years. If the initial cost of the car was $27,985, what was the value after 5 years?

A. $19.235 **B.** $27.885 **C.** $8.750 **D.** $36.635

7.NS.A.3

15. An elevator is on the nineteenth floor. It goes down 7 floors and then up 4 floors. What floor is it on now?

____

7.NS.A.3

16. Melissa took a test. For each question she answered incorrectly, she lost 1 point and for every question she answered correctly, she earned 2 points. If there were 25 questions on the test and she answered 4 incorrectly, what was Melissa's final score?

____

7.NS.A.3

17. Isaac woke up with a fever of 101.8 degrees Fahrenheit. Two hours later, it was 3 degrees lower. What was his new temperature, in degrees Fahrenheit?

____

7.NS.A.3

18. A boat is pulling a diver up to the surface at a rate of 24 feet per minute. If the diver is 180 feet below the surface, how long will it take the boat to pull her to the surface?

______

______

7.NS.A.3

19. It is 6 degrees Fahrenheit outside and the temperature will drop 13 degrees during the next 8 hours. How cold, in degrees Fahrenheit, will it be 8 hours from now?

______

______

7.NS.A.3

20. Lindsay has $82 in her checking account. She deposits $45. Then, She writes a check for $96. What is her new balance?

______

______

7.NS.A.3

CHAPTER REVIEW

1. A company sold 60 cars in September. In October, the company sold 23 cars. In November, the company received 28 cars from the manufacturer. If the company had 89 cars at the beginning of September, how many cars did the company have at the end of November?

A. 116 **B.** 0 **C.** 91 **D.** 34

(7.NS.A.1)

2. Liam and Morgan are scuba diving. Liam is 12 meters below the surface and Morgan is 5.3 meters above Liam. What is Morgan's depth relative to the surface of the water?

A. −6.7m **B.** 6.7m **C.** 17.3m **D.** −17.3m

(7.NS.A.1)

3. If $n = -3$ and $m = -5$, which expression has a positive value?

A. $n+m$ **B.** $n-m$ **C.** $m-n$ **D.** $m+n$

(7.NS.A.1)

4. If $a = -6$ and $b = -9$, what is $-b-a$?

A. 15 **B.** −15 **C.** −3 **D.** 3

(7.NS.A.1)

5. Which expression is equivalent to 48 − (23)?

A. 23 − 48 **B.** 23 + 48 **C.** 48 − 23 **D.** 48 + 23

(7.NS.A.1)

6. Sam has \$189 in the bank. He uses a bank card to buy an Xbox for \$220. How much money does he owe the bank?

____

(7.NS.A.1)

CHAPTER REVIEW

7. John had $\frac{5}{8}$ of a pizza and wanted to divide it between his two brothers. How much of the whole pizza will each brother get?

A. $\frac{6}{10}$ **B.** $\frac{5}{8}$ **C.** $\frac{1}{4}$ **D.** $\frac{5}{16}$

7.NS.A.2

8. Which fraction is equal to $-\frac{15}{4}$?

A. $\frac{-15}{4}$ **B.** $\frac{15}{4}$ **C.** $\frac{-4}{15}$ **D.** $-\frac{4}{15}$

7.NS.A.2

9. Evaluate the following expression: $(-9 \div 3) + \frac{1}{2}(-8-2)$

A. -8 **B.** -11 **C.** 4 **D.** 7

7.NS.A.2

10. Evaluate the following expression: $(\frac{3}{4} \times 12) + (-9 \div 3) - 2\frac{1}{8}$

A. 3 **B.** 6 **C.** $-2\frac{3}{8}$ **D.** $3\frac{7}{8}$

7.NS.A.2

11. A farmer has 300 bags of seeds to sell at a market. He sells an average of $15\frac{3}{4}$ bags each day. How many bags does the farmer have after 6 days?

____

7.NS.A.2

12. A company's stock sold for \$84.75. Six days later, the same stock sold for \$62.25. What was the average change in the stock value per day?

____

7.NS.A.2

13. After hiking to the top of a mountain, Michael descends at a rate of -380 feet per hour. Which equation represents his change in elevation after 80 minutes?

A. $380 \times 1\frac{1}{3}$ **B.** $-380 \times (1\frac{1}{3})$ **C.** 380×80 **D.** 380×-80

(7.NS.A.3)

14. A dolphin is swimming at the surface of the ocean. He dives at a rate of 4 feet per minute. If water level represents an elevation of 0 feet, what number represents the dolphin's depth after $2\frac{1}{2}$ minutes?

A. 10 feet **B.** 8 feet **C.** -10 feet **D.** -8 feet

(7.NS.A.3)

15. At 8:00 pm, the temperature was 37 degrees Fahrenheit. By 4:00 am, the temperature was -2 degrees Fahrenheit. What was the total change in temperature during those 8 hours?

A. 35 degrees Fahrenheit **B.** 39 degrees Fahrenheit
C. -35 degrees Fahrenheit **D.** -39 degrees Fahrenheit

(7.NS.A.3)

16. Which expression has the same value as $-\frac{1}{8} \div -\frac{6}{16}$?

A. $-\frac{1}{8} \times -\frac{16}{6}$ **B.** $\frac{1}{8} \times \frac{16}{6}$ **C.** $8 \times \frac{6}{16}$ **D.** $-\frac{1}{8} \times \frac{16}{6}$

(7.NS.A.3)

17. Eli bought 4 pounds of bananas for $0.69 per pound and Peyton bought 3 pounds of bananas for $0.74 per pound. Who spent the most money?

A. Eli **B.** Peyton
C. They spent the same amount. **D.** You need additional information.

(7.NS.A.3)

CHAPTER REVIEW

Ace Academic Publishing
ACHIEVING EXCELLENCE TOGETHER

CHAPTER REVIEW

18. Riza is diving and is ascending at a rate of 0.75 feet per second. If he was originally at −23 feet below the surface, how long will it take for him to reach the surface?

(7.NS.A.3)

19. In summer, the average temperature on the South Pole is approximately −18 degrees Fahrenheit. The average temperature at the North Pole is approximately 32 degrees Fahrenheit. What is the difference between the two temperatures?

(7.NS.A.3)

20. Mount McKinley is 20,237 feet above sea level. The lowest point in North America is in Death Valley and is −282 feet below sea level. What is the difference in the two elevations?

(7.NS.A.3)

EXTRA PRACTICE

1. Point A is located at $-4\frac{2}{3}$ on a number line. Point B is $12\frac{2}{3}$ units to the right of Point A. Which number represents Point B?

A. $8\frac{1}{3}$ B. $-17\frac{1}{3}$ C. 8 D. 16

7.NS.A.1

2. The distance between Point X and Point Z on a number line is 48 units. Point Y is $\frac{3}{4}$ of the distance from Point X to Point Z. Which numbers could represent Points X, Y, and Z

A. Point X: 12, Point Y: 48, Point Z: 60

B. Point X: 20, Point Y: 72, Point Z: 116

C. Point X: 15, Point Y: 40, Point Z: 63

D. Point X: 16, Point Y: 40, Point Z: 48

7.NS.A.1

3. Which expression has the same value as $-5(-14.3-8.1)$?

A. $-5(14.3+8.1)$ B. $5(14.3-8.1)$

C. $-5(14.3+8.1)$ D. $-5(-14.3+(-8.1))$

7.NS.A.1

4. Sarah has \$382 in her bank account on Saturday. Two days earlier, she made a deposit of \$147, and a withdrawal of \$85. How much money was in Sarah's bank account two days earlier?

____

7.NS.A.1

EXTRA PRACTICE

EXTRA PRACTICE

5. Mark this value on the number line below:

$$2(-4+8-2)$$

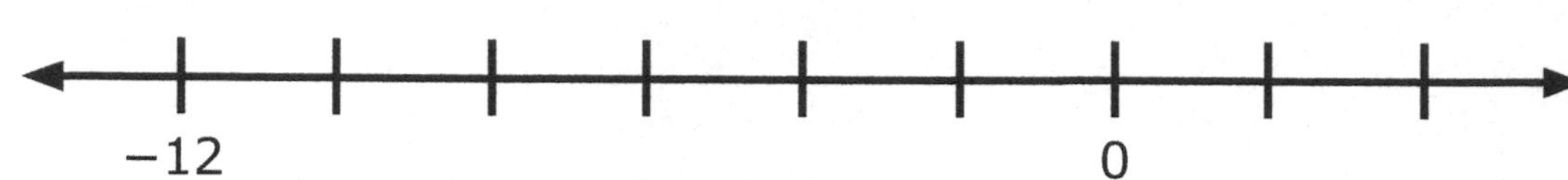

(7.NS.A.1)

6. The distance between Point R and Point J on this number line is 14 units. If Point J is greater than Point R, what is its value?

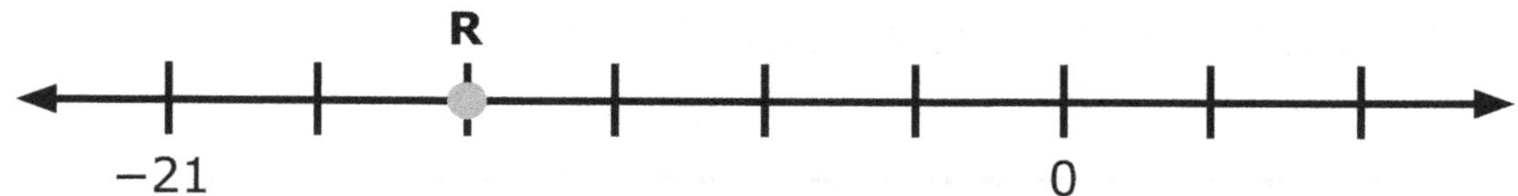

____

(7.NS.A.1)

7. Explain how you would simplify this expression:

$$-0.75+(-\tfrac{1}{8})+2.25$$

____

____

____

(7.NS.A.1)

EXTRA PRACTICE

8. Jessica believes the fraction $\frac{4}{9}$ is equivalent to $(9 \div 2) \times 2$. Do you agree with Jessica? Explain your reasoning.

____

____

____

(7.NS.A.2)

9. Where does $0.\overline{27}$ belong on the number line?

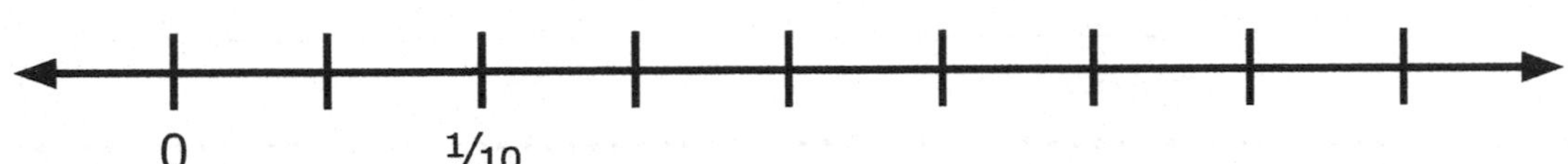

(7.NS.A.2)

10. If the expression $-m + 2m$ has a negative value, and m is an integer. Write an inequality to represent the value of m.

____

(7.NS.A.2)

11. Willie says all fractions with a denominator of 9 are repeating decimals. Do you agree? State your reasoning.

____

____

____

(7.NS.A.2)

EXTRA PRACTICE

12. What is the value of this expression?

$$\left(-\frac{4}{7}\right) \div \frac{8}{21} \times \left(-3\frac{1}{5}\right)$$

____

(7.NS.A.2)

13. A number x is divided by 4, added to $\frac{15}{4}$, and multiplied by -3. The result is $-11\frac{11}{20}$. What is the value of x?

____

(7.NS.A.2)

14. Tim says 0.825 divided by $\frac{1}{4}$ can be determined using this expression:

$$825 \div 250$$

Do you agree with Tim? Explain your reasoning.

____

____

____

(7.NS.A.2)

15. Write an expression to represent the distance, in miles, between the school and grocery store.

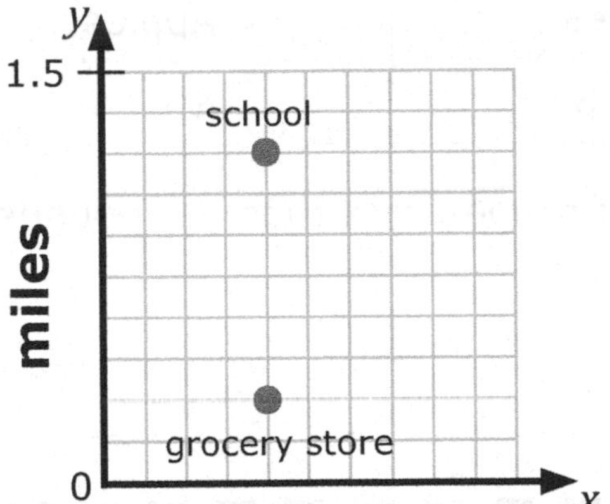

(7.NS.A.3)

16. Cecil and his 2 friends charge $17.50 per hour for tutoring. Each person spends 4 hours tutoring, and they spend 10% of their combined income on supplies. How much money does each person make, after buying supplies?

(7.NS.A.3)

17. How would you solve this expression? Write your steps on the lines below.

$$\frac{\frac{1}{3}}{\left(-\frac{4}{5}\right)} \div \frac{2}{5}$$

(7.NS.A.3)

EXTRA PRACTICE

18. This table shows the cost of grapes and apples at the grocery store.

Fruit / Vegetable	Grapes	Apples
Cost per Pound	$1.48	$1.24

How much more does $2\frac{1}{4}$ pounds of grapes cost than $2\frac{1}{4}$ pounds of apples?

____

7.NS.A.3

19. This table shows the cost of bananas and strawberries at the grocery store.

Fruit / Vegetable	Bananas	Strawberries
Cost per Pound	$0.68	$1.54

What is the cost of $1\frac{5}{8}$ pounds of bananas and 3 pounds of strawberries?

____

7.NS.A.3

20. The length of a rectangle is $11\frac{2}{3}$ centimeters. The width is twice the length. What is the perimeter of the rectangle?

____

7.NS.A.3

EXPRESSIONS AND EQUATIONS

EQUIVALENT EXPRESSIONS	65
EXPRESSIONS AND EQUATIONS WORD PROBLEMS	73
CONSTRUCT EQUATIONS AND SOLVE WORD PROBLEMS	80
CHAPTER REVIEW	89
EXTRA PRACTICE	98

phi
Y

1. Which strategy can be used to simplify this expression?

$$4x + 3x - 5 - 2x$$

A. Add $4x$, $3x$, and $2x$.

B. Subtract $2x$ from the sum of $4x$ and $3x$.

C. Subtract 5 from $3x$.

D. Subtract $2x$ from -5.

(7.EE.A.1)

2. Which strategy can be used as a first step in simplifying this expression?

$$3(5y + 6) - 4(2y)$$

A. Add 3 and $5y$.

B. Add $5y$ and 6.

C. Multiply $5y$ and 6 by 3.

D. Subtract 4 from 6.

(7.EE.A.1)

3. Cynthia is simplifying this expression.

$$4x - 3 - 9x - 1$$

Cynthia decides to subtract $9x$ from $4x$ as her first step.

Why is she correct?

A. Cynthia is combining like terms.

B. There is a total of 4 terms in this expression.

C. Subtraction is the only operation used in this expression.

D. The variable used in this expression is x.

(7.EE.A.1)

4. Henri is simplifying this expression.

$$\frac{5}{7} + \frac{1}{3} + \frac{2}{7} \times \frac{2}{3}x$$

Henri decides to multiply $\frac{2}{7}$ and $\frac{2}{3}x$ as his first step. Why is this correct?

A. The fractions $\frac{2}{7}$ and $\frac{2}{7}$ have the same denominator.

B. The fraction $\frac{2}{3}$ contains a variable.

C. Order of operations dictates to multiply before adding.

D. The expression does not contain parentheses.

(7.EE.A.1)

5. Ivan measures the distance around this playground.

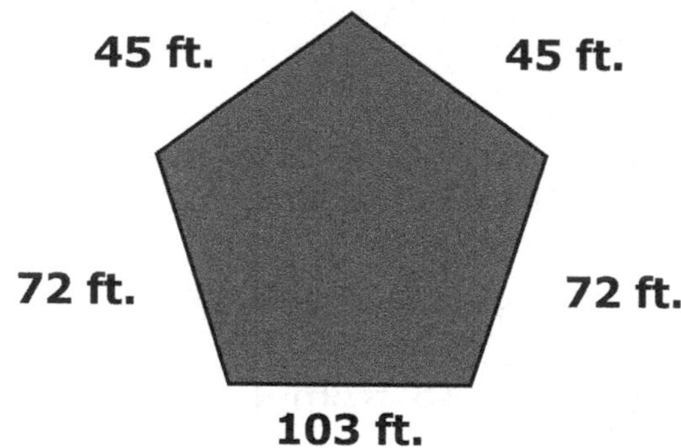

Which expression represents the total distance around the playground?

A. $2(103) + 2(45) + 2(72)$

B. $2(45 + 72 + 103)$

C. $2(45 + 72) + 103$

D. $2(72) + 2 + 45 + 103$

(7.EE.A.1)

EQUIVALENT EXPRESSIONS

6. Lorene draws this triangle.

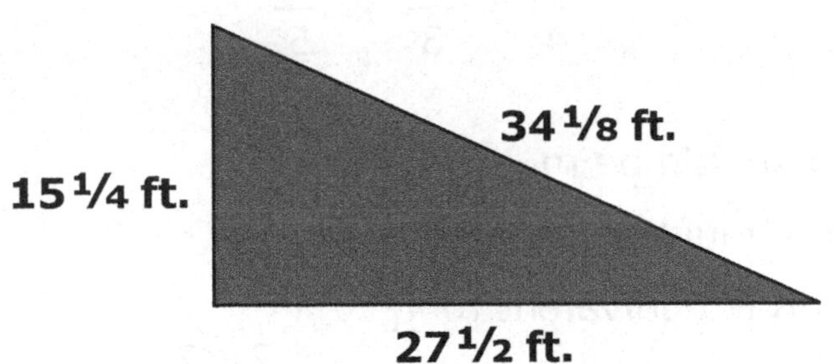

Lorene draws a second triangle with each side 3 feet longer than the first triangle.

Which expression represents the perimeter of the second triangle?

A. $(15\frac{1}{4}+3)+(34\frac{1}{8}+3)+(27\frac{1}{2}+3)$

B. $(15\frac{1}{4}+3)+(34\frac{1}{8}+3)+27\frac{1}{2}$

C. $3(15\frac{1}{4}+34\frac{1}{8}+27\frac{1}{2})$

D. $3(15\frac{1}{4})+3(34\frac{1}{8})+3(27\frac{1}{2})$

(7.EE.A.1)

7. Which expression is equivalent to the expression shown below?

$$\frac{1}{5} \times [8+4(\frac{1}{2}+5)]$$

A. $\frac{1}{5} \times (17\frac{1}{2})$

B. $\frac{1}{5} \times (30)$

C. $\frac{1}{5} \times (32\frac{1}{2})$

D. $\frac{1}{5} \times (15)$

(7.EE.A.1)

EQUIVALENT EXPRESSIONS

8. Which statement about this expression is true?

$$\frac{1}{4} \div \frac{2}{3} \times \frac{2}{5}$$

A. The first step should be multiply $\frac{2}{3}$ by $\frac{2}{5}$.

B. The first step should be divide $\frac{1}{4}$ by $\frac{2}{3}$.

C. The expression is equivalent to $\frac{15}{16}$.

D. The expression has the same value as $\frac{2}{5} \cdot \frac{2}{3} \div \frac{1}{4}$.

7.EE.A.1

9. Which expression can be used to find the area of Triangle ABD?

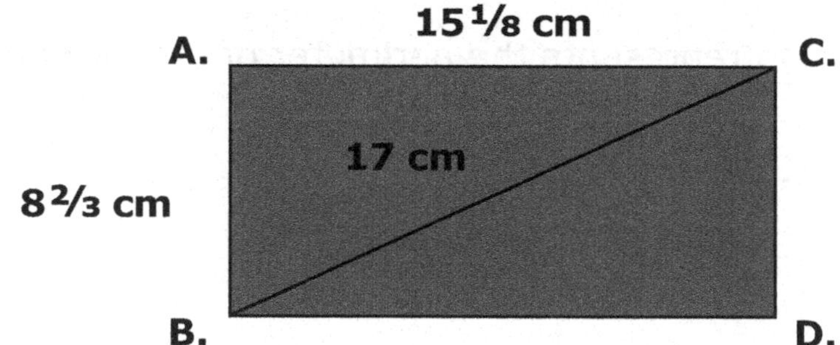

A. $\frac{(8\frac{2}{3} \cdot 15\frac{1}{8})}{2}$

B. $8\frac{2}{3} + 15\frac{1}{8} + 17$

C. $\frac{1}{2}(8\frac{2}{3} \cdot 17)$

D. $2(8\frac{2}{3} + 15\frac{1}{8})$

7.EE.A.1

10. This expression represents the sum of three consecutive integers.

$$x + (x + 1) + (x + 2)$$

Write an equivalent expression.

____

7.EE.A.1

EQUIVALENT EXPRESSIONS

11. The perimeter of a square is $20x+8$ inches.

Which expression can be used to represent one side length of this square?

A. $80x+32$ inches

B. $10x+16$ inches

C. $24x+12$ inches

D. $5x+2$ inches

(7.EE.A.1)

12. The perimeter of a square is $32x+16$ inches. Which expression can be used to represent one side length of this square?

A. $128x+64$ inches

B. $16x+8$ inches

C. $8x+4$ inches

D. $28x+12$ inches

(7.EE.A.1)

13. The perimeter of a square is $24+8x$ inches.

Which strategy can be used to find the length of each side of this square?

A. Multiply 24 and $8x$ by 4

B. Add 4 to 24 and $8x$

C. Divides 24 and $8x$ by 8

D. Divide 24 and $8x$ by 4

(7.EE.A.2)

14. The distance around a building is $10x+25+5x$ feet. Which expression represents the distance halfway around the building?

A. $\frac{15x+25}{2}$

B. $(10x+25+5x)-\frac{1}{2}$

C. $\frac{1}{2}(40x)$

D. $\frac{15x+25}{(\frac{1}{2})}$

(7.EE.A.2)

EQUIVALENT EXPRESSIONS

15. The length of a rope is $30 + 27x - 12x$ yards. The rope is cut into 3 equal pieces. Which expression represents the length of one piece?

A. $\frac{30 + 15x}{(\frac{1}{3})}$

B. $\frac{30 + 15x}{3}$

C. $\frac{1}{3}(45x)$

D. $(30 + 27x - 12x) - \frac{1}{3}$

(7.EE.A.2)

16. Sales tax in a state is 8.25%. Which expression represents the total cost of an item m after sales tax is added?

A. $0.0825m$

B. $1 + 1.0825m$

C. $1.0825m$

D. $8.25m$

(7.EE.A.2)

17. Sales tax in a state is 9.45%. Which expression represents the total cost of an item m after sales tax is added?

A. $m + 0.0945m$

B. $0.0945m$

C. $1 + 1.0945m$

D. $9.45m$

(7.EE.A.2)

18. This table shows the sales tax rates in 5 different states.

State	Sales Tax Rate (Percentage)
Tennessee	9.45
Louisiana	8.91
Washington	8.89
Texas	8.25
Arkansas	9.26

...question 18. continued next page

Which expression represents the difference in the cost of an item x in Louisiana and the cost of the same item in Texas after sales tax is added?

A. $8.91x - 8.25x$

B. $0.0066x$

C. $x + 0.0891x + x + 0.0825x$

D. $0.66x$

(7.EE.A.2)

19. This table shows the sales tax rates in 5 different states.

State	Sales Tax Rate (Percentage)
Tennessee	9.45
Louisiana	8.91
Washington	8.89
Texas	8.25
Arkansas	9.26

Which expression represents the cost of an \$8.89 item in Washington after sales tax is added?

A. $1(0.0889)$

B. $8.89 + (8.89)(8.89)$

C. $1.889\ (8.89)$

D. $8.89 + (0.0889 \cdot 8.89)$

(7.EE.A.2)

EQUIVALENT EXPRESSIONS

20. Xavier invests x dollars into a bank account. This expression represents the total amount of money in Xavier's bank account after 1 year.

$$x + 0.125x$$

What is the interest rate on this account?

A. 0.125%

B. 0.875%

C. 12.5%

D. 87.5%

(7.EE.A.2)

1. Mr. Henry has $215 in his bank account. This table shows the bills he must pay this month using the money in his account.

Bill	Amount Due (Dollars)
Telephone	57
Electricity	125
Water	32
Gasoline	91

How much money will Mr. Henry have in his bank account after he pays his bills?

A. $90 **B.** $305 **C.** –$90 **D.** $520

7.EE.B.3

2. Eric spends $85 buying 2 identical shirts, 1 pair of pants, and a hat. The pants and hat were the same price, and cost Eric $19 each.

What is the price of each shirt?

A. $23.50 **B.** $47.00 **C.** $66.00 **D.** $33.00

7.EE.B.3

3. Mr. Henry has some money in his bank account. This table shows the bills he must pay this month using the money in his account.

Bill	Amount Due (Dollars)
Telephone	62.15
Electricity	142.70
Water	84.95
Gasoline	77.50

...question 3. continued next page

WORD PROBLEMS

He has $125.03 remaining after paying his bills. How much money was in Mr. Henry's bank account before he paid his bills?

A. $242.27 **B.** $492.33 **C.** $367.30 **D.** –$242.27

(7.EE.B.3)

4. Linh spent $135.04 on 4 shirts, 2 pairs of socks, and 1 pair of pants. Each shirt cost $21.99, and a pair of socks cost $4.75.

What was the cost of the pair of pants?

A. $42.33 **B.** $108.30 **C.** $37.58 **D.** $103.55

(7.EE.B.3)

5. Pooja used a credit card to buy a new phone which cost $706.94. The credit card company will not charge interest if she pays off the balance in $3\frac{1}{2}$ years.

She pays $95.00 towards the balance and plans to pay the rest over time in equal monthly payments. How much money should Pooja pay each month?

A. $611.74 **B.** $14.57 **C.** $174.78 **D.** $16.83

(7.EE.B.3)

6. Lamont used a credit card to buy a new phone which cost $595.84. The credit card company will not charge interest if he pays off the balance in 18 months. He pays $112.00 towards the balance and plans to pay the rest over time in equal monthly payments.

Which expression can be used to determine the amount of money Lamont will pay each month?

A. $595.87 - 112 - 18$ **B.** $\frac{595.87}{18}$

C. $595.87 - 112$ **D.** $\frac{595.84 - 112}{18}$

(7.EE.B.3)

WORD PROBLEMS

7. What is the value of this expression?

$$-24+6(14-8)$$

____

(7.EE.B.3)

8. The temperature in a city decreases 22 degrees between 5pm and 9pm, then rose 18 degrees by 9am the next morning.

If the temperature at 9am is −3°, what was the temperature at 5pm on the previous day?

A. 1°F **B.** −7°F **C.** 37°F **D.** 7°F

(7.EE.B.3)

9. The temperature in a city decreases 2°F each hour between 6pm in the evening and 3am the next morning.

If the temperature at 3am is −11°F, what was the temperature at 6pm on the previous day?

A. −9°F **B.** −2°F **C.** 7°F **D.** 5°F

(7.EE.B.3)

10. William builds a clock in 184.2 hours. He spends 2.6 hours constructing each hand of the clock.

William's clock has an hour, minute, and second hand. He spends the rest of the time building the clock's frame.

How much time does he spend building the clock's frame?

A. 181.6 hours **B.** 7.8 hours **C.** 61.4 hours **D.** 176.4 hours

(7.EE.B.3)

NAME: .... DATE: ....

EXPRESSIONS AND EQUATIONS

WORD PROBLEMS

11. Mrs. Johnson's floral shop contains 78 varieties of roses. The roses are grouped into 3 categories: Wild Roses, Old Garden Roses, and Modern Garden Roses.

One-sixth of the roses are Old Garden Roses, and $\frac{1}{3}$ of the roses are Wild Roses.

How many roses are Modern Garden Roses?

A. 26 **B.** 39 **C.** 13 **D.** 75

7.EE.B.3

12. What is the value of this expression?

$$\frac{1.6}{(1.8+3.2)} + (3.7-1.25)$$

____

7.EE.B.3

13. A farmer collects 8 bushels of apples. Each bushel contains 126 apples. If she sells $2\frac{1}{2}$ bushels to a local store, how many apples does she have left?

____

7.EE.B.3

14. The distance from the cafeteria to the band hall is 748 ft. The distance from the band office to the cafeteria is $\frac{1}{4}$ this distance, but in the opposite direction. What is the total distance, in feet, from the band office to the band hall? Show your work.

____

____

____

7.EE.B.3

15. A farmer collects 13 bushels of peaches. Each bushel contains 132 peaches. If he sells $4\frac{1}{2}$ bushels to a local store, how many peaches does the farmer have left? Show your work.

7.EE.B.3

16. The distance from the cafeteria to the band hall is 696 ft. The distance from the band office to the cafeteria is $\frac{5}{6}$ this distance, in the same direction.

What is the difference, in feet, between the distance from the band office to the cafeteria and the distance from the cafeteria to the band hall? Show your work.

7.EE.B.3

EXPRESSIONS AND EQUATIONS

WORD PROBLEMS

17. Ama has $319. She spent half of the money on a new video game, put $55 in her bank account, and spent the rest on clothes.

How much money did Ama spends on clothes? Show your work.

(7.EE.B.3)

18. Philip is estimating the value of this expression.

$$205(148-36)+14-824$$

He decides to use this compatible number strategy

$$200(150-40)+10-800$$

How far from the correct answer is Philip's estimate?

(7.EE.B.3)

WORD PROBLEMS

19. Xavion is surveying the students in his middle school. There are 358 students in sixth grade, 310 students in seventh grade, and 402 students in eighth grade.

If Xavion wants to survey 20% of the students in each grade level, what is the approximate number of students he should survey? Show you work.

____

____

____

7.EE.B.3

20. There are 40 players on a baseball team. Nineteen of the players are from the United States. One-fourth of the players are from Caribbean islands. The remaining players are from the Central America.

How many players are from Caribbean islands and how many players are from Central America? Explain your reasoning.

____

____

____

7.EE.B.3

1. This table shows the pizza prices at a restaurant.

Pizza Size	Small	Medium	Large
Cost (Dollars)	10	14	18

The sales tax is 8.45%, and the restaurant is offering a $1.99 discount off the total price when more than 1 pizza is ordered.

Which equation represents x, the cost of ordering 1 small and 2 large pizzas?

A. $((10-1.99)+(18(2)-1.99))(1.0845)=x$

B. $[(10+18(2))(1.0845)]-1.99=x$

C. $(10+18+18)+(10+18+18)(0.0845)=x$

D. $(10+18+18)(1.0845)(1.99)=x$

7.EE.B.4

2. This table shows the additional food prices at a restaurant.

Item	Salad	Additional Toppings	Drink
Cost (Dollars)	5.99	0.50 each	2

If sales tax is 8.25%, which equation represents x, the cost of ordering a salad with 5 additional toppings, and 1 drink?

A. $(5.99+2.50+2)(8.25)=x$

B. $(5.99+2.50+2)=x$

C. $(5.99+2.50+2)+(5.99+2+2.50)(0.0825)=x$

D. $(5.99+2.50+2)+1.0825=x$

7.EE.B.4

3. Khalid and his 4 friends are competing in a fundraiser. Altogether, they must walk at least 100 miles in one month.

They walk 12 miles the first week and decide to divide the remaining miles equally between them.

Which inequality can be used to determine x, the number of miles each person must walk to meet their goal?

A. $4x + 12 \geq 100$ **B.** $5x - 12 \geq 100$

C. $12x \geq 100$ **D.** $12 + 5x \geq 100$

(7.EE.B.4)

4. Riley is raising money for a fundraiser. She plans to raise \$20 each week.

Which inequality can be used to determine the number of weeks y Riley must raise money to meet a goal of at least \$500?

A. $20y \geq 500$ **B.** $20y \leq 500$

C. $20 \geq 500y$ **D.** $20 \leq 500y$

(7.EE.B.4)

5. Sarah writes this inequality to represent the amount of money she needs to earn over x weeks for a fundraiser.

$$15x + 30 \geq 150$$

What does 30 represent in this inequality?

A. The total amount of money Sarah needs to raise.

B. The amount of money Sarah will raise each week.

C. The amount of money Sarah has already raised.

D. The number of weeks Sarah will raise money.

(7.EE.B.4)

6. A classroom has 10 desks and some tables. Five students sit at each table, and there are 35 students in the class.

Which equation can be used to determine the number of tables m needed for the students in this class?

A. $5m + 10m = 35$ **B.** $5 + 10 = 35m$

C. $5 + 10m = 35$ **D.** $5m + 10 = 35$

7.EE.B.4

7. A classroom has round and square tables. Eight students can sit at each round table, and 4 students can sit at each square table. There are 28 students in the class and 3 square tables.

Which equation can be used to determine the number of round tables m needed for the students in this class?

A. $(28 - 12) \div 8 = m$ **B.** $8m + 4m = 28$

C. $28 = 3(8) + 4m$ **D.** $m = 28 - 8 - 4$

7.EE.B.4

8. A chemical in a science experiment dissolves at a rate of 1.025 grams per second. The chemical dissolves in 15.4 seconds. What was the original mass of the chemical?

A. 15.785 grams **B.** 16.4254 grams

C. 14.375 grams **D.** 15.02 grams

7.EE.B.4

9. A chemical in a science experiment dissolves at a rate of 0.984 grams per second. The chemical has a weight of 18.75 grams. Which equation represents t the number of seconds it takes for the chemical to dissolve?

A. $(18.75)(0.984) = t$

B. $18.75 \div 0.984 = t$

C. $18.75 + 0.984 = t$

D. $18.75 - 0.984 = t$

7.EE.B.4

10. Eriko wants to save $650. He has $125 and plans to save $17.50 each month. Write an equation to determine x, the number of months it will take Eriko to save $650.

____

7.EE.B.4

11. Armand is participating in a 7 – day hike. This table shows the distance he travels over the first 4 days.

Day	1	2	3	4
Distance (miles)	5.8	12.1	8.9	10.5

The entire hike is more than 50 miles. Write an inequality to represent x the number of miles he must travel each day to finish the hike.

____

7.EE.B.4

12. Yesenia wants to run more than 15 miles in 6 days. On the first day, she ran 2.5 miles.Write an inequality to represent how many more miles x Yesenia needs to run each day.

____

7.EE.B.4

13. Tori is taking a trip from Los Angeles to Chicago. This map shows the route she will travel.

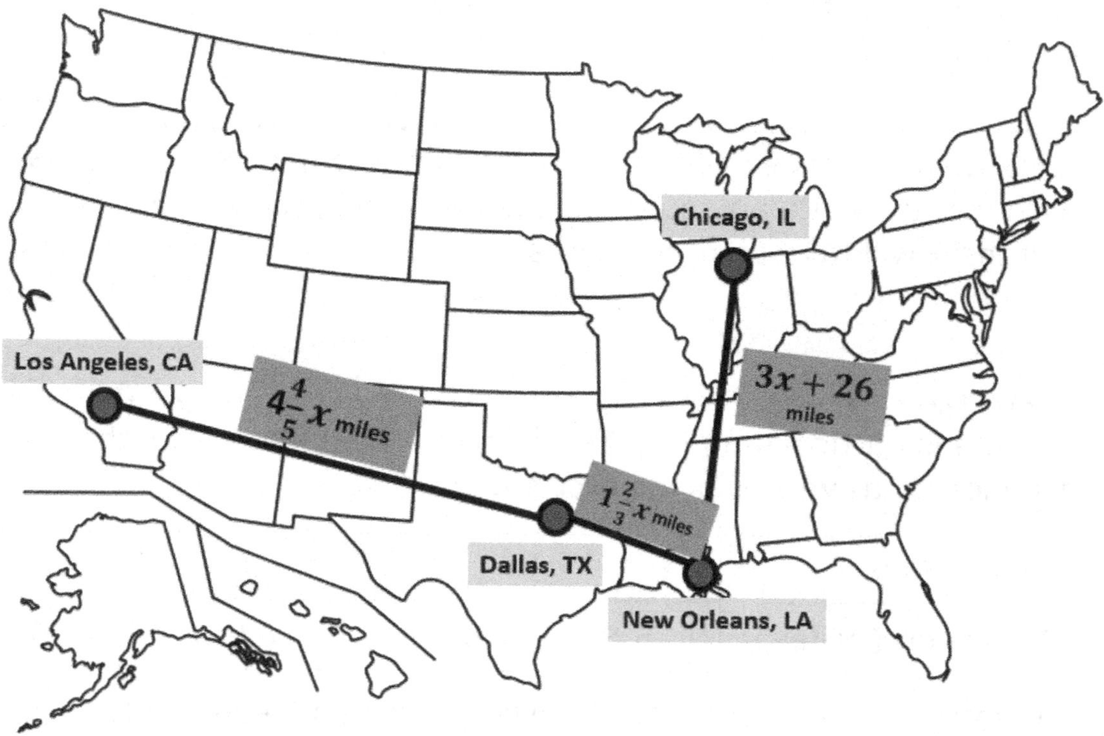

The distance from Los Angeles to Dallas is 1,440 miles. How many miles will Tori travel on this trip?

____

7.EE.B.4

14. A pilot flew from New York to Billings, and then to Chicago. This map shows his flight path.

The distance between Billings and Chicago is $\frac{2}{3}$ the distance between Billings and New York.

How far, in miles, is Billings from Chicago?

____

(7.EE.B.4)

CONSTRUCT EQUATIONS AND SOLVE WORD PROBLEMS

15. The perimeter of a rectangle is 82.94 centimeters. One pair of parallel sides have a combined length of 46.48 centimeters.

What is length and width of this rectangle? Include units.

______

7.EE.B.4

16. The perimeter of this figure is 180 cm.

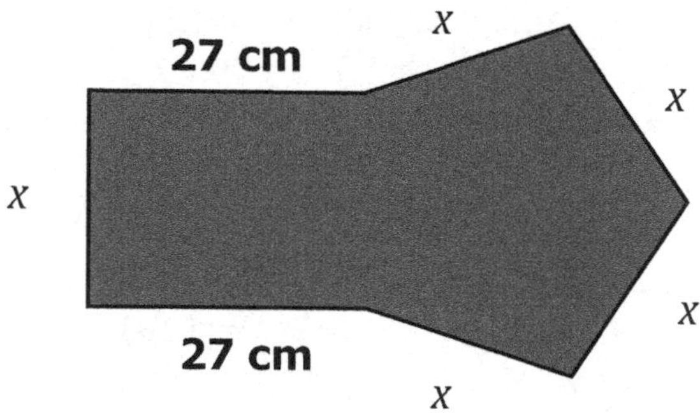

What equation can be used to find the missing values?

______

______

______

______

______

7.EE.B.4

17. Write an equation to determine the number of 3-pound weights needed to balance this scale.

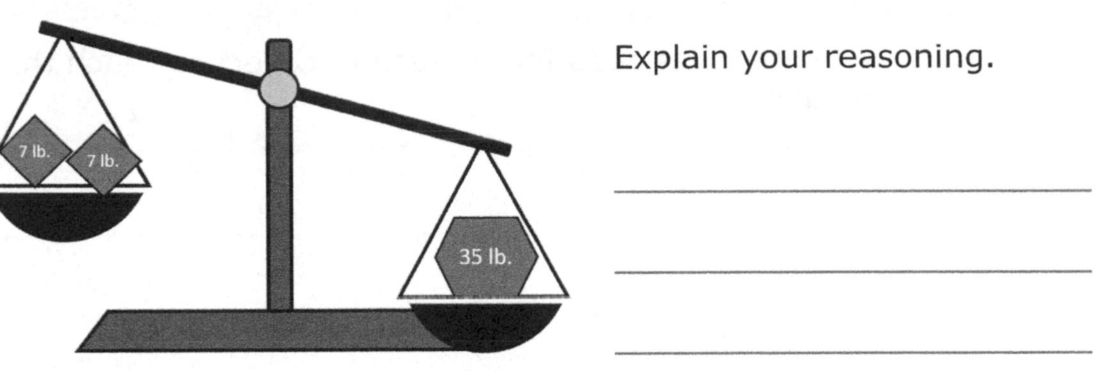

Explain your reasoning.

____

____

____

____

____

(7.EE.B.4)

18. Write an inequality to compare the weights shown on this balance.

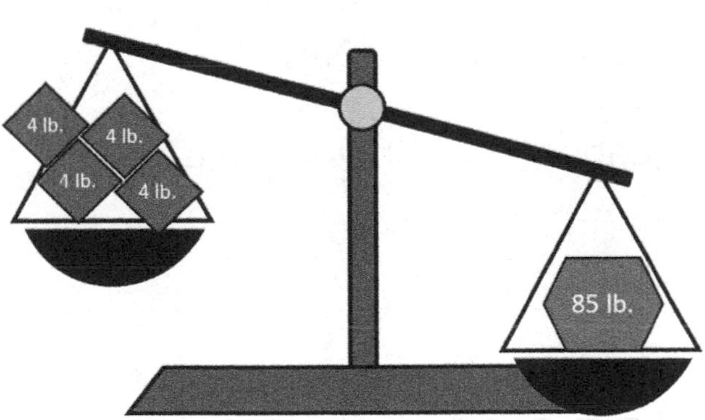

What equation could determine the number of 3-pound weights needed to balance this scale? Explain your reasoning.

____

____

____

____

____

(7.EE.B.4)

19. Ingrid is playing a video game where every 2 coins collected gives her 45 points. She has collected 195 points and needs 1,365 points to reach the next level.

How many more coins does Ingrid need to collect to reach the next level of the game?

____

____

____

(7.EE.B.4)

20. Tyson has a collection of 35 pennies, 19 nickels, and some dimes which total $2.40.

He uses this equation to determine the number of dimes x he has in his collection.

$$0.01(35) + (5)(19) + (10)(x) = 2.40$$

Do you agree with Tyson's equation? Explain your reasoning.

____

____

____

(7.EE.B.4)

1. The map shows the distance Evi travels from Boise, Idaho to Miami, Florida.

Which expression represents the total distance Evi travels?

A. $62m$ miles

B. $50+12m$ miles

C. $3(45+5m)(3m+5)(2m+2m)$ miles

D. $50m+8m+4m$ miles

7.EE.A.1

2. Which algebraic expression correctly interprets this verbal expression?

Three times the sum of a number and 6.

A. $3x+18$ **B.** $3+x+6$ **C.** $3(x)(6)$ **D.** $(3x)+6$

7.EE.A.1

3. Which algebraic expression correctly interprets this verbal expression? Seven times a number minus the sum of six and five times the number

A. $7y-6(5y)$

B. $(7y-6)+5y$

C. $2y-6$

D. $y+5y$

(7.EE.A.1)

4. The length of one side of a hexagon is this expression.

$$10+4x-(5x-5)$$

Write the step-by-step process you can use to write a simplified expression, with no groupings, for the perimeter of this hexagon.

____

____

____

(7.EE.A.1)

5. The length of one side of a pentagon is is this expression.

$$(3x-30)+4x$$

Write the step-by-step process you can use to write a simplified expression, with no groupings, for the perimeter of this pentagon.

____

____

____

(7.EE.A.1)

CHAPTER REVIEW

6. Factor this expression.

$$(72x + 120 + 432)$$

____

____

____

____

7.EE.A.1

7. Belinda bought 3 pairs of shoes from the store.

If t represents the cost of one pair of shoes, which expression represents the total amount of money Belinda spent at the store?

A. $3t$ **B.** $0.5t$ **C.** $2.5t$ **D.** t

7.EE.A.1

8. A store is selling items at a discount. This expression is the original price of the item p with a 7.5% discount.

$$p - 0.075p$$

Which expression is amount of the discount?

A. $1.075p$ **B.** $0.075p$ **C.** $0.25p$ **D.** $1.925p$

7.EE.A.1

9. Maya is buying school supplies, and the subtotal of the items she is buying is x dollars. She has a coupon for 20% off her entire order and says this expression provides the total amount of money she will spend.

$$0.20x$$

Do you agree with Maya? Explain your reasoning.

____

____

____

____

(7.EE.A.2)

10. Avery is buying school supplies, and the cost of her items is x dollars. She has a coupon for 35% off her entire order and says this expression can be used to represent the total amount of money she will spend.

$$0.65x$$

Do you agree with Avery? Explain your reasoning.

____

____

____

____

(7.EE.A.2)

11. Write an expression in Column B that is equivalent to the one shown in Column A.

Column A	Column B
$2(4x+8)-2$	

Describe the process you would use to create the equivalent expression.

____

____

____

____

(7.EE.A.2)

12. Are these expressions equivalent? Explain your reasoning.

$$98.2m-14m-m$$

$$84.2m$$

____

____

____

____

____

(7.EE.A.2)

13. This table shows the number of students at a middle school and the percentage of students who travel to school by bus.

Grade Level	Number of Students	Students Traveling by Bus (Percent)
6	400	75
7	390	60
8	405	80

Which expression represents the number of 7th and 8th grade students traveling to school by bus?

A. $(60 \cdot 390)+(80 \cdot 405)$
B. $(390+405)(140)$
C. $(0.60 \cdot 390)+(0.80 \cdot 405)$
D. $(390+405)(1.4)$

7.EE.A.2

14. A restaurant opens at 6 am. Before 11 am, the restaurant serves 21 people each hour, and the restaurant serves 38 people every half hour between 11 am and 2 pm. They serve 28 people each hour after 2pm and close at 4 pm.

How many people does the restaurant serve between 6am and 4pm?

____

____

____

7.EE.A.2

15. This table shows the number of students at a middle school and the percentage of students who ride a bus to school.

Grade Level	Number of Students	Students Riding a Bus (Percent)
6	400	75
7	390	60
8	405	80

How many more 8th grade students than 6th grade students ride a bus?

A. 5 **B.** 24 **C.** 90 **D.** 19

7.EE.B.3

16. A hiker is traveling across a mountain range. This table shows the distance traveled and location of the hiker each day.

Day	Distance Traveled (feet)	Elevation (feet)
Monday	15,359	15,359
Tuesday	10,035	11,847
Wednesday	6,115	8,335
Thursday	178	?

If the elevation continues to change the same amount each day, at what elevation, in feet, is the hiker on Thursday?

____

7.EE.B.3

17. A chemical in a science experiment dissolves in 31.04 seconds.

The chemical has a mass of 36.32 grams. At what rate does the chemical dissolve?

A. 5.15 grams per second
B. 0.86 grams per second
C. 1.17 grams per second
D. 0.52 grams per second

(7.EE.B.4)

18. Elijah creates this graph on the number line to model the changes in the amount of money he has in his investment account.

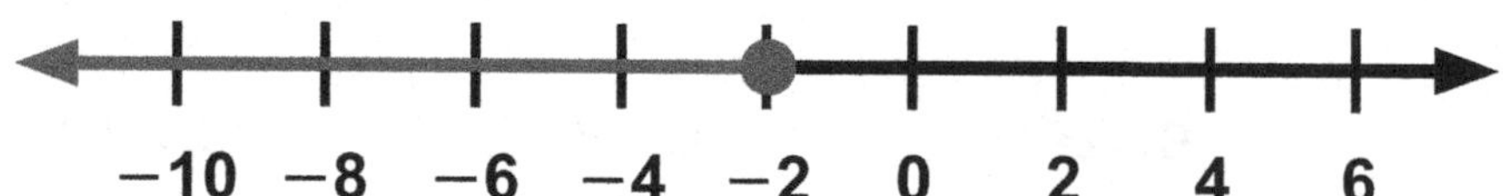

Which inequality represents the changes in his account?

A. $x \leq -2$
B. $x \geq -2$
C. $x < -2$
D. $x > -2$

(7.EE.B.4)

19. The perimeter of this hexagon is 101.5 centimeters.

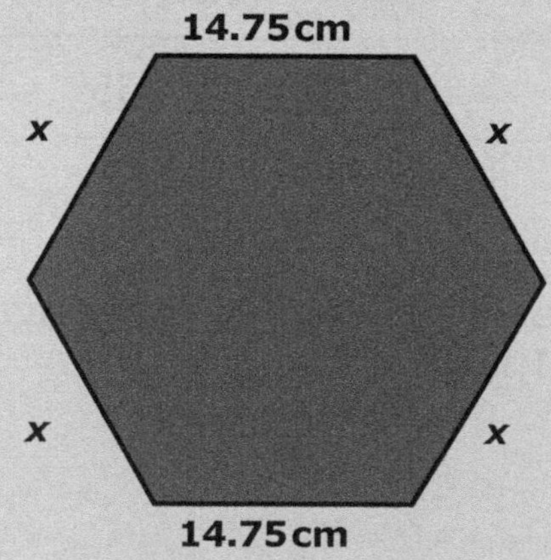

What is the value of x?

____

(7.EE.B.4)

20. Orel has a collection of some pennies, 12 nickels, and 21 dimes which total $4.00.

He uses this equation to determine the number of pennies x he has in his collection.

$0.01(x) + (0.05)(12) + (0.1)(21) = 4.00$

Do you agree with Orel's equation? Explain your reasoning.

____

____

____

7.EE.B.4

EXTRA PRACTICE

EXPRESSIONS AND EQUATIONS

1. This map shows the route Jessi's family flew from Los Angeles, California to Chicago, Illinois.

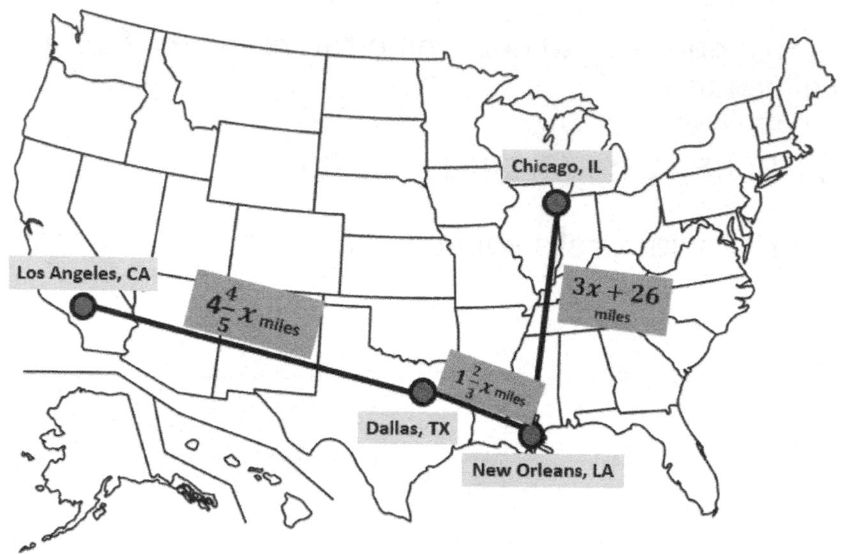

Which expression represents the total distance flown?

A. $(8\frac{6}{8}x + 26)$ miles

B. $35\frac{7}{15}x$ miles

C. $(4\frac{4}{5})(1\frac{2}{3})(3x + 26)$ miles

D. $(9\frac{7}{15}x + 26)$ miles

7.EE.A.1

2. Translate this statement into an algebraic expression.

The product of eight and the difference of six and three times a number

____

____

7.EE.A.1

3. A science fair project requires 3 pieces of cardboard.

- The longest piece of cardboard is 3 times the length of the middle piece.
- The shortest piece is 12 inches shorter than the middle piece.

Which expression could be used to represent the combined length of all 3 pieces if the length of the middle piece is x inches?

A. $3x+x+(x-12)$ inches
B. $3x+x+x+12$ inches
C. $3x+(x-12)$ inches
D. $3x-12+x$ inches

7.EE.A.1

EXTRA PRACTICE

4. Write an algebraic expression to represent the total number of degrees in this circle.

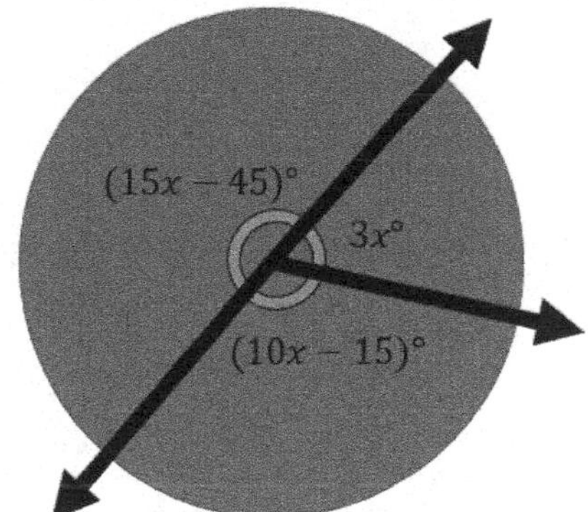

____

____

7.EE.A.1

EXTRA PRACTICE

5. Write an expression to represent the total number of degrees in this circle.

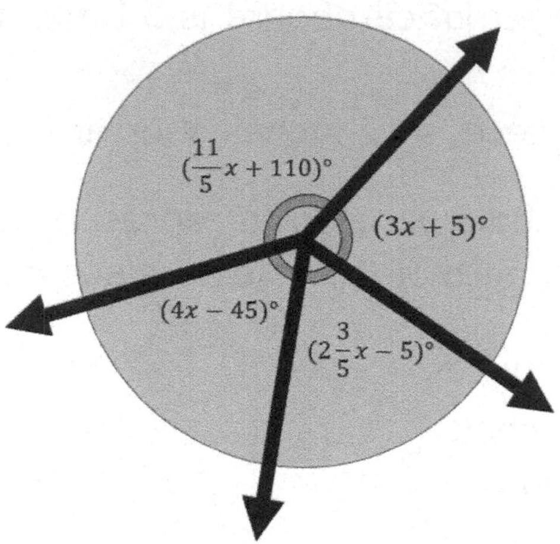

____

7.EE.A.1

6. The length of one side of a hexagon is represented by this expression.

$$4(2x-8)$$

Write an expression to represent the perimeter of this hexagon.

____

7.EE.A.1

7. Hotdogs cost \$3 and hamburgers cost \$4. Sales tax is 8.75%. Write an expression to represent the total cost of x hotdogs and y hamburgers.

____

7.EE.A.2

8. The length of a piece of rope is $9x(\frac{1}{3}+\frac{1}{6})$ feet. The rope is cut into 3 equal pieces. Write an expression to represent the length of one piece.

____

(7.EE.A.2)

9. The distance between Points A and C on this circle is $14x+18+6x$ centimeters.

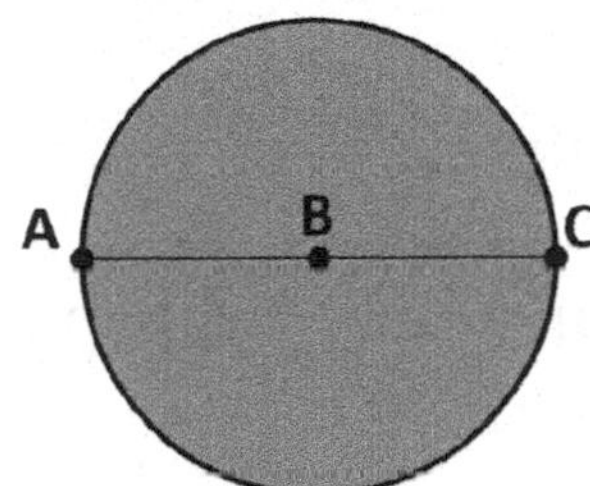

Point B marks the center of the circle. What is the distance from Point A to Point B?

(7.EE.A.2)

10. This expression describes how the original body temperature m of a sick animal changed over two days.

$$0.9(1.13m)$$

How would you describe this change?

____

____

____

(7.EE.A.2)

EXTRA PRACTICE

EXTRA PRACTICE

11. This expression describes how the original body temperature m of a sick animal changed over two days.

$$1.05\ (0.95m)$$

How would you describe this change?

___

___

___

(7.EE.A.2)

12. Are these expressions equivalent? Explain your reasoning.

$$d + 0.75d + 0.25d$$

$$2d$$

___

___

___

(7.EE.A.2)

13. There are 25 active players on a baseball team. Thirteen of the players are from the United States. Two-fifths of the players are from Cuba. The remaining players are from the Caribbean islands.

How many players are from the Caribbean islands?

A. 2 **B.** 10 **C.** 12 **D.** 23

(7.EE.B.3)

14. Elliot has $1,425 in a bank account. He plans to spend $\frac{4}{10}$ of his money on a new musical instrument and $\frac{1}{20}$ of his money buying sheet music.

How much money will Elliot have left?

____

(7.EE.B.3)

EXTRA PRACTICE

15. A hiker is traveling across a mountain range. On Monday morning, the hiker starts at sea level. This table shows the distance traveled and location, or elevation, at the end of the day, for each day.

Day	Distance Traveled (feet)	Elevation (feet)
Monday	18,179	2,179
Tuesday	13,922	4,964
Wednesday	17,827	?
Thursday	15,345	10,534

Assuming the same change in elevation each day, at what elevation, in feet, is the hiker on Wednesday? Is the hiker above or below sea level? Explain your reasoning.

____

____

____

(7.EE.B.3)

EXTRA PRACTICE

16. Miley's dog weighs 3 times as much as her cat. Her bird is $\frac{1}{28}$ the weight of her cat. The cat weighs 8.12 pounds. How much does the dog weigh, in pounds? How much does the bird weigh, in ounces? Show your work.

7.EE.B.3

17. This table shows the pizza prices at a restaurant.

Pizza Size	Cost (Dollars)
Small	10
Medium	14
Large	18

Abby spends $32.10 at this pizza restaurant buying 3 pizzas that are the same size. Sales tax is 7%. Which equation can be used to determine the amount of money x Abby spends on each pizza before tax is added?

A. $32.10-(0.07)(3x)=x$

B. $\frac{32.10}{3}=1.07x$

C. $3x+0.07(x)=32.10$

D. $3x+7(3x)=32.10$

7.EE.B.4

18. A paper company produces 238,000 sheets of paper. A machine organizes the paper into 42 packages of 500 sheets each hour.

How long will it take for the machine to package 238,000 pieces of paper?

A. 12 hours

B. 10.33 hours

C. 11.33 hours

D. 72 hours

7.EE.B.4

19. This table shows the relationship between the dimensions of a rectangle and its perimeter.

Length	Width	Perimeter
4	1	10
4	2	12
4	3	14
4	4	16
4	5	18
4	6	20
4	7	22

Which equation can be used to find the width x of a rectangle with a length of 4 units and a perimeter of 30 units?

A. $2(4)+4x=30$

B. $(2)(4)+2x=30$

C. $30-(2)(4)=x$

D. $30+2(4)=x$

7.EE.B.4

EXTRA PRACTICE

20. Yesenia wants to run more than 15 miles in 6 days. On the first day, she ran 2.5 miles.

Draw a number line to model the number of miles she still needs to run.

Explain your reasoning.

7.EE.B.4

GEOMETRY

DRAW AND UNDERSTAND GEOMETRIC FIGURES 109

AREA, SURFACE AREA, AND VOLUME 119

ANGLE PAIRS 128

CHAPTER REVIEW 136

EXTRA PRACTICE 143

1. Irina is traveling from Dallas to New York. This map shows the route she travels.

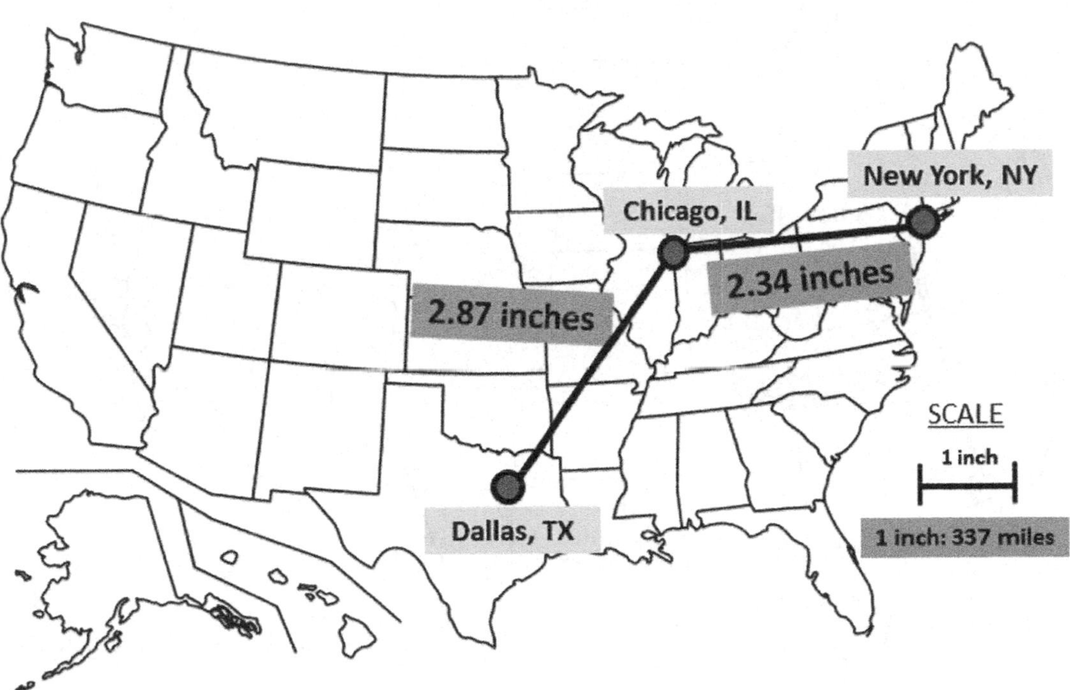

How many miles does Irina travel?

A. 967 miles
B. 1.756 miles
C. 789 miles
D. 337 miles

(7.G.A.1)

2. Pavati traveled from Los Angeles, California to Boise, Idaho. This map shows the route she traveled.

How many miles did Pavati travel?

A. 337 miles

B. 228 miles

C. 768 miles

D. 674 miles

7.G.A.1

3. Aiguo is planning a road trip. This map shows Seattle, Washington, where he lives, as well as the cities he plans to visit.

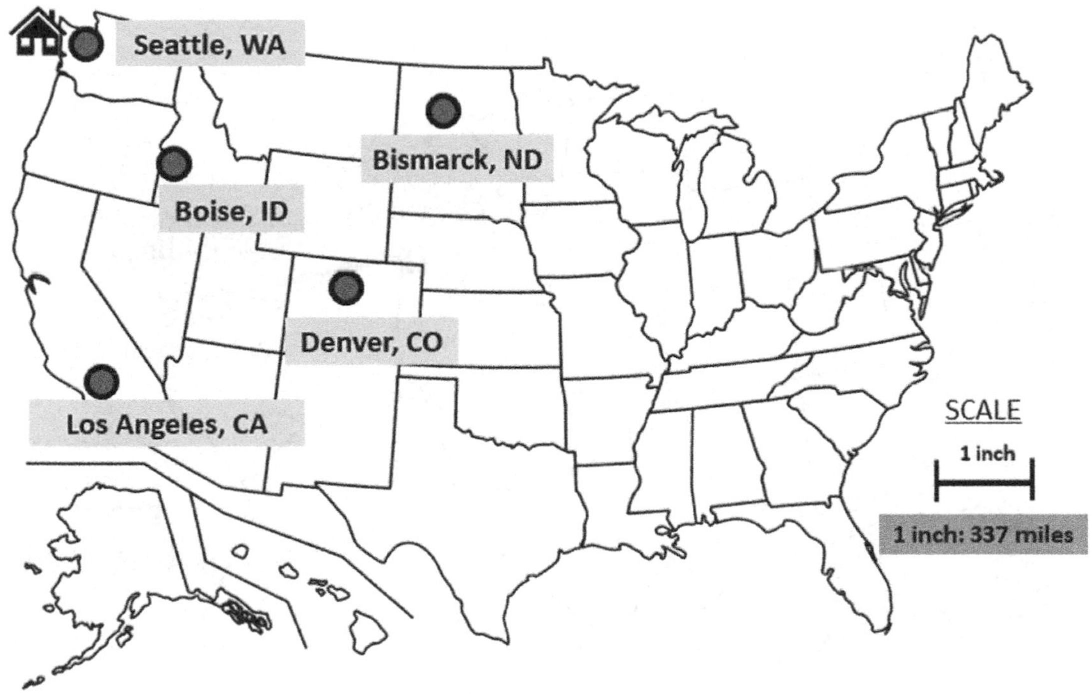

Aiguo wants to travel between 1,200 and 1,300 miles. Which city should he visit?

A. Boise, ID
B. Denver, CO
C. Los Angeles, CA
D. Bismarck, ND

7.G.A.1

4. This map shows the distance between Washington, D.C., and Chicago, Illinois.

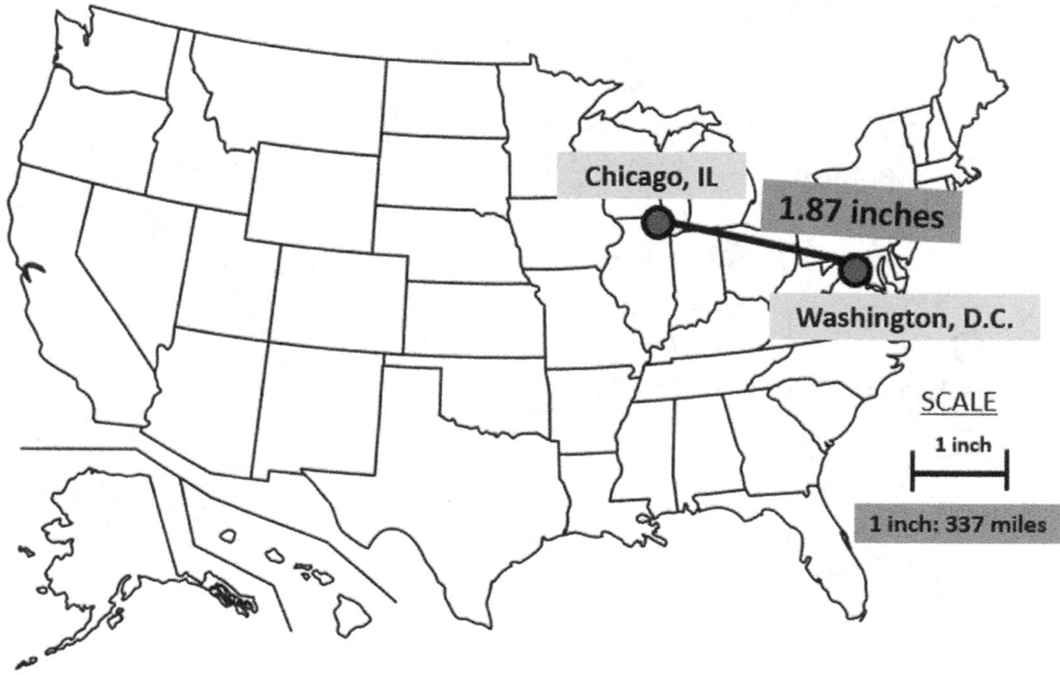

Which strategy shows how you could determine the number of miles between these two cities?

A. 337(1.87)

B. 337 + 1.87

C. 337 ÷ 1.87

D. 337 − 1.87

7.G.A.1

5. Zoe uses this scale to create a model of the Empire State Building.

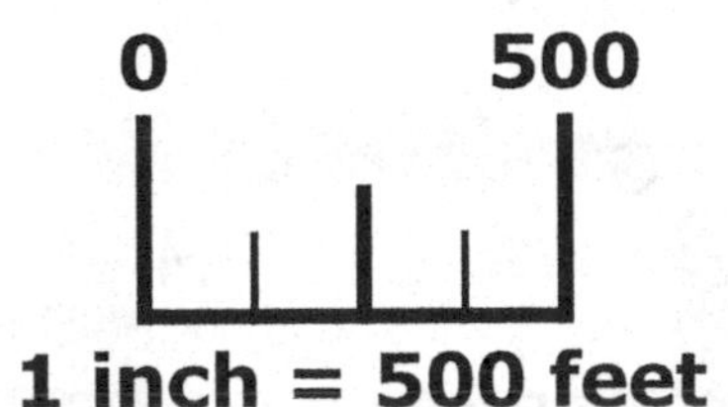

The height of the Empire State Building is 1,454 feet. What is the height, to the nearest tenth of an inch, of Zoe's model?

____

(7.G.A.1)

6. Parallelogram ABCD is similar to Parallelogram RSTV.

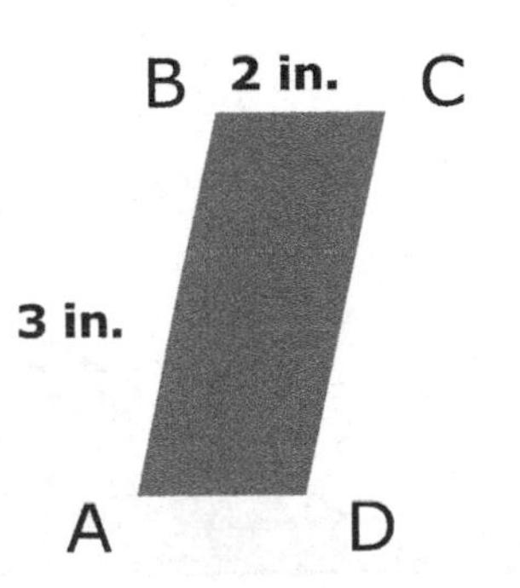

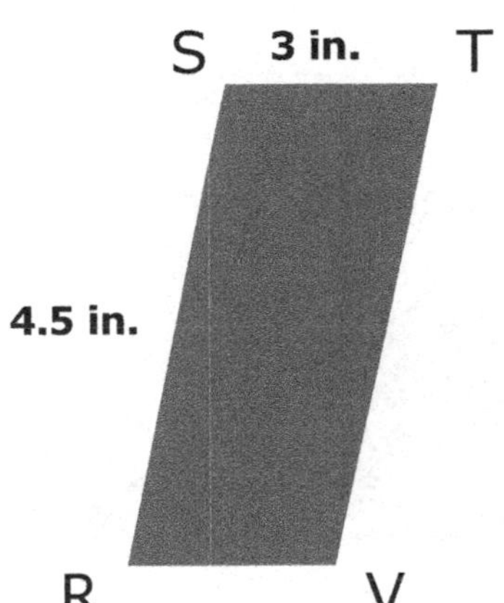

What scale factor is used to create Parallelogram RSTV from Parallelogram ABCD?

____

(7.G.A.1)

7. Rectangle FGHJ is similar to Rectangle MNOP.

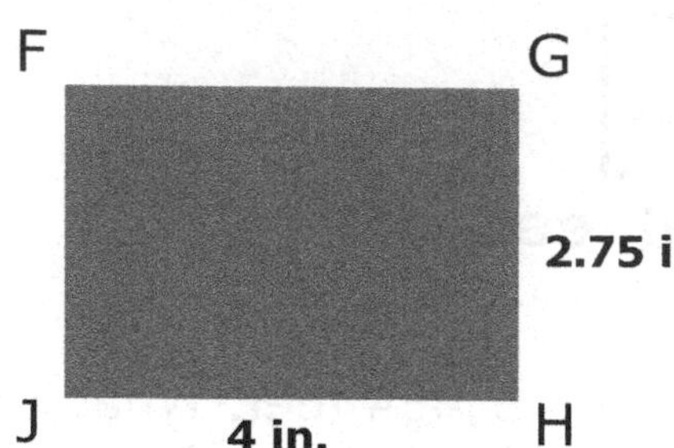

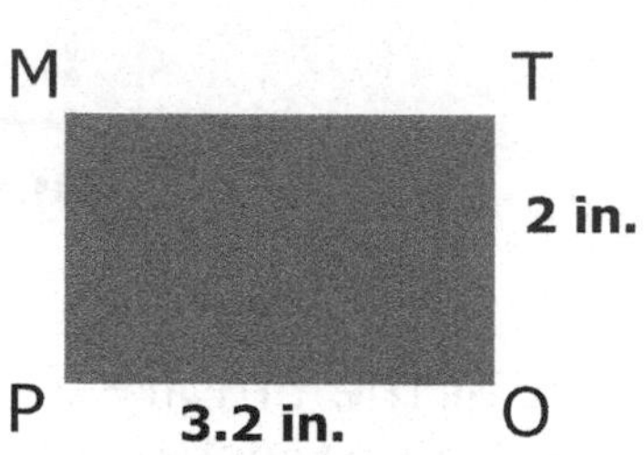

What scale factor is used to create Rectangle MNOP from Rectangle FGHJ?

____

(7.G.A.1)

8. Which triangle has angle measures of 45°, 45°, and 90°?

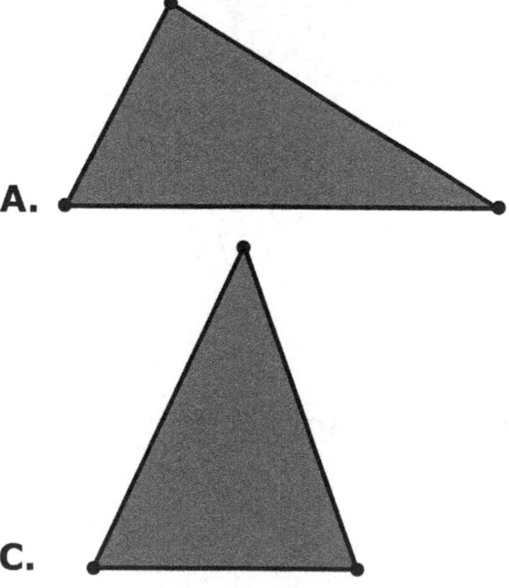

A.

C.

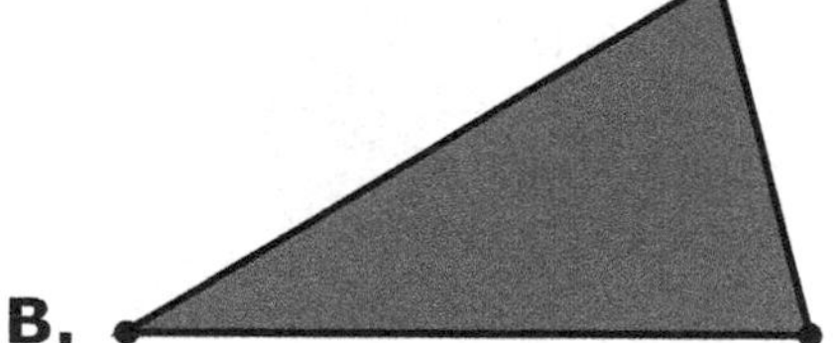

B.

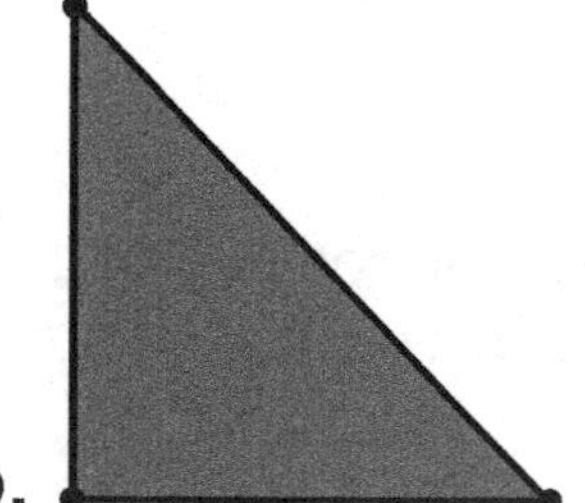

D.

(7.G.A.2)

GEOMETRY

9. Which angle measures represent an acute scalene triangle?

A. 50°, 95°, 35° **B.** 75°, 75°, 30°
C. 35°, 60°, 85° **D.** 60°, 60°, 60°

7.G.A.2

10. Which angle measures represents an equilateral triangle?

A. 60°, 60°, 60° **B.** 50°, 50°, 80°
C. 30°, 60°, 90° **D.** 100°, 40°, 40°

7.G.A.2

11. Which angle measures represents an obtuse scalene triangle?

A. 100°, 40°, 40° **B.** 90°, 30°, 60°
C. 25°, 75°, 80° **D.** 30°, 35°, 115°

7.G.A.2

12. Cleveland is using the two angles shown on these protractors to construct a triangle.

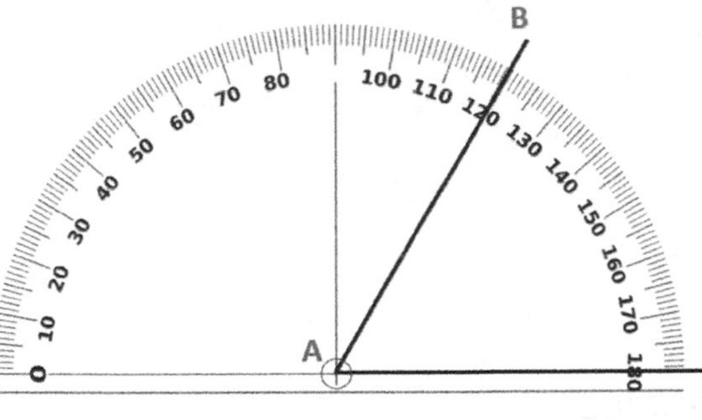

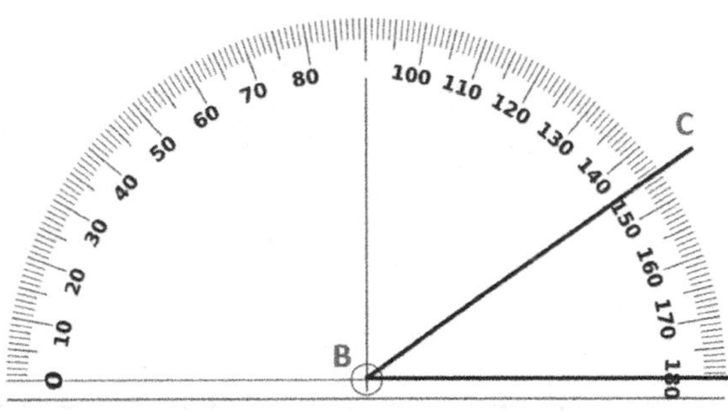

What is the measure of the third angle?

A. 35° **B.** 60° **C.** 85° **D.** 145°

7.G.A.2

DRAW AND UNDERSTAND GEOMETRIC FIGURES

13. Peter is using the angles shown in these protractors to construct a triangle.

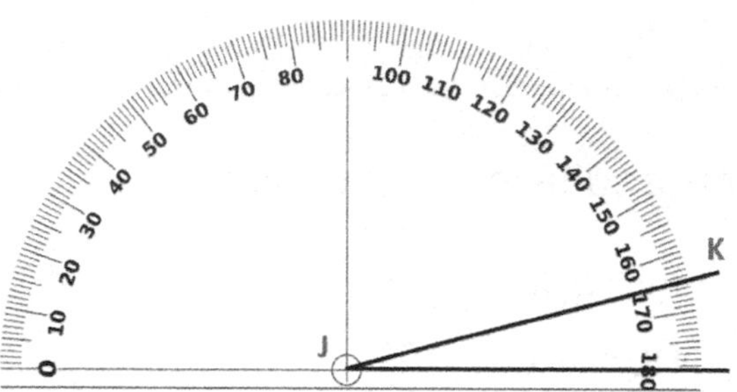

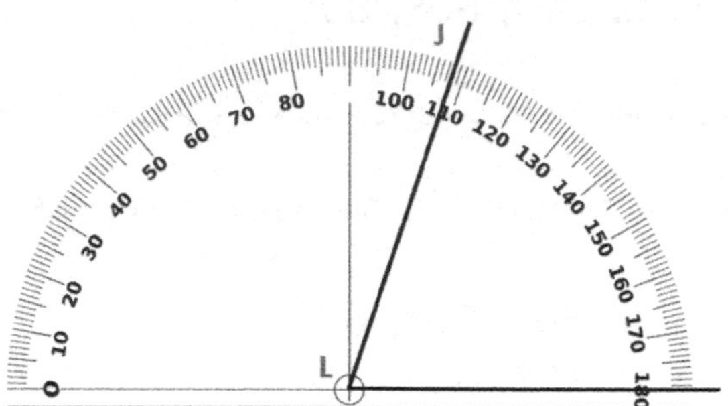

What is the measure of the third angle?

____

(7.G.A.2)

14. Brian is using this protractor to construct obtuse isosceles ΔRST.

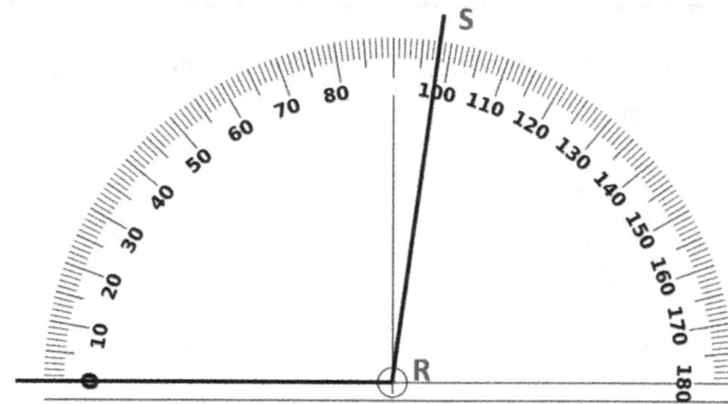

What is the measure of the acute angles?

____

(7.G.A.2)

15. Jamal is constructing a triangle. The length of shortest side is 7 inches, and the length of another side is 11 inches.

What are the possible whole number lengths, in inches, of the triangle's third side?

____

(7.G.A.2)

16. Which shape describes the cross-section created when this solid is sliced perpendicular to its base?

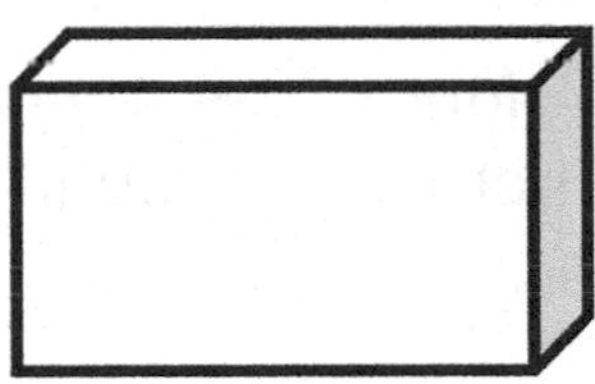

A. square
B. rectangle
C. rhombus
D. hexagon

(7.G.A.3)

17. Which shape describes the cross-section created when this solid is sliced parallel to its base?

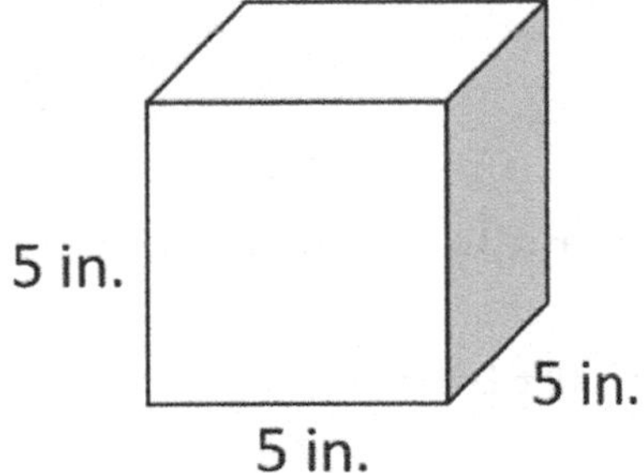

A. cube **B.** hexagon **C.** rhombus **D.** square

(7.G.A.3)

18. Points A, B, and C are equidistant from each adjacent vertex on this cube.

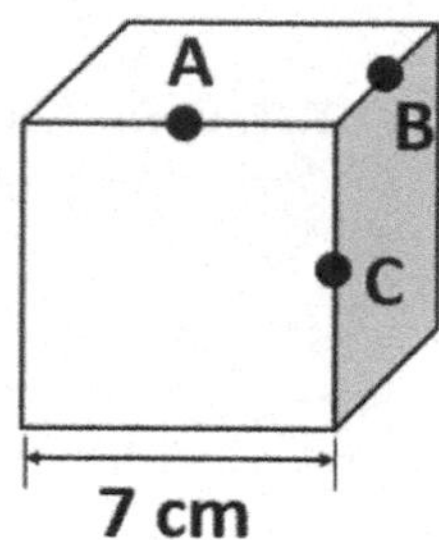

What shape is created by slicing the cube through Points A, B, and C?

____

(7.G.A.3)

19. Chaundra creates a cross section by slicing a right rectangular pyramid perpendicular to its base, that does not pass through the vertex of the pyramid.

Which shape does Chaundra create?

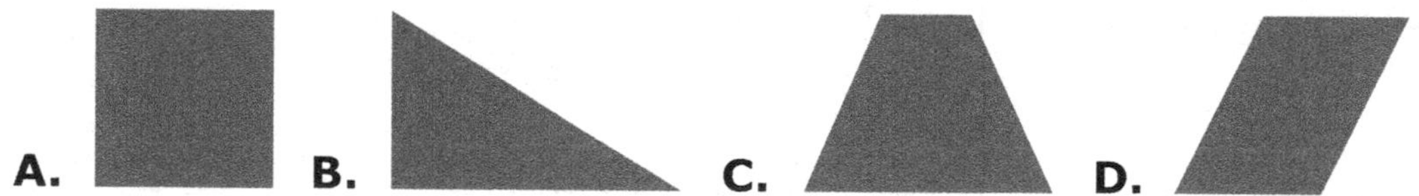

(7.G.A.3)

20. Bart slices a cube diagonally through 5 of its faces.

Which shape does Bart create?

____

(7.G.A.3)

1. Bailey is walking around this lake to see the turtle habitat on the opposite side of the lake.

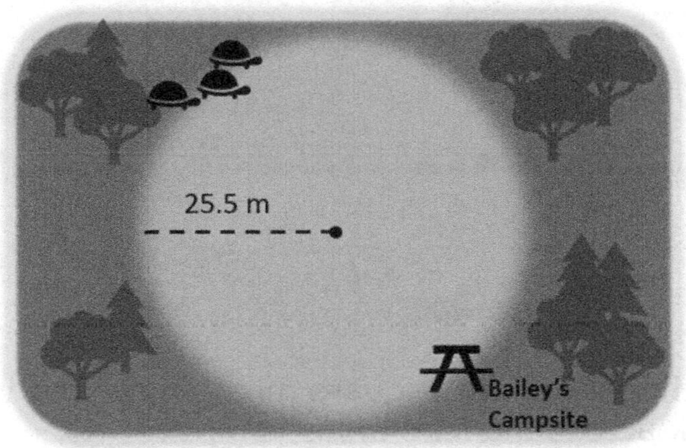

How far does Bailey walk from his campsite to the turtle habitat?

A. 80.07 m **B.** 40.04 m **C.** 78.5 m **D.** 51 m

7.G.B.4

2. What is the area of this pond?

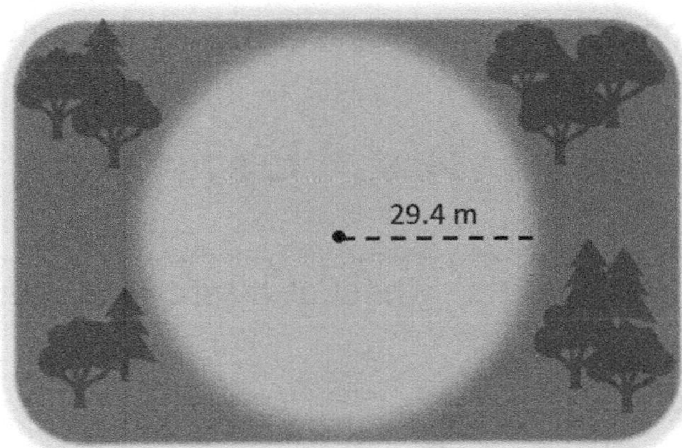

A. 92.32 m^2 **B.** 184.63 m^2 **C.** 2,714.09 m^2 **D.** 10,856.36 m^2

7.G.B.4

3. Brian kayaks from his campsite across this lake at a speed of 5 miles per hour.

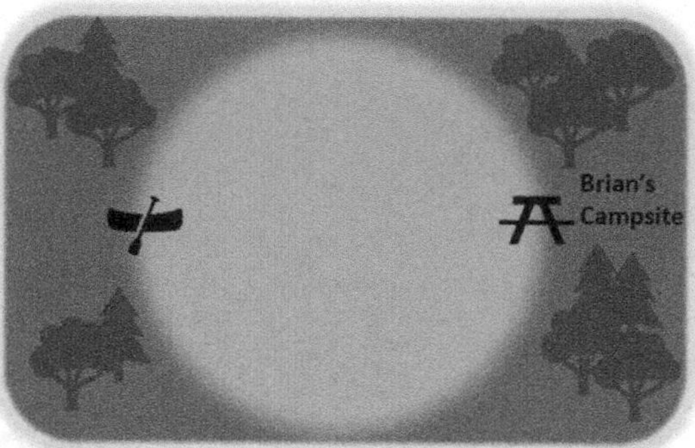

The area of the lake is 15.9 square miles. How long will it take Brian to travel back across the lake to his campsite?

A. 2.25 hours **B.** 4.5 hours **C.** 0.9 hours **D.** 3.18 hours

7.G.B.4

4. A circular playground has a circumference of 65.94 yards. Mr. Helene plans to fill the playground with a layer of rubber mulch. Each bag of mulch costs $12 and covers 1 square yard.

How much money will Mr. Helene spend on enough mulch to cover the entire playground?

A. $16,616.88 **B.** $4,154.22 **C.** $791.28 **D.** $346.19

7.G.B.4

5. A hamster runs inside this wheel at a rate of 22 centimeters per second.

How long will it take for the wheel to make one full turn?

A. 2.3 seconds **B.** 2.8 seconds
C. 1.1 seconds **D.** 9.1 seconds

7.G.B.4

6. Mr. Alexian is gathering ingredients to prepare 24 frosted donuts. The recipe he uses recommends 0.12 grams of frosting for each square inch of dough. Each circular donut has a diameter of 5.75 inches.

How many grams of the frosting does Mr. Alexian need to prepare?

A. 75 **B.** 150 **C.** 104 **D.** 52

7.G.B.4

7. Xavier determines that the circumference of a circle is π feet.

What is the length of the circle's radius?

____

7.G.B.4

8. Josie calculates that the circumference of a circle is $\frac{\pi}{3}$ yards. What is the area of this circle?

____

7.G.B.4

9. This table shows the relationship between the circumference and diameter of several circular objects.

Object	Circumference (inches)	Diameter (inches)
Clock	36.11	11.5
Penny	2.36	0.75
Nickel	2.64	0.84
Dime	2.23	0.71
Button	8.17	2.6

...question 9. continued next page

What is the ratio of the circumference to the diameter of a circular object?

______

______

______

(7.G.B.4)

10. A circle has a radius with the length of 13 feet.

What is the ratio of the area of this circle to the circumference of this circle?

______

______

______

(7.G.B.4)

11. This rectangle is the base of a prism.

The ratio of the height of a prism to the area of its base is $\frac{1}{4}$. What is the volume of this prism, in cubic centimeters?

A. 41.25 cubic centimeters

B. 495 cubic centimeters

C. 6,806.25 cubic centimeters

D. 108,900 cubic centimeters

(7.G.B.6)

12. This rectangle is the base of a prism.

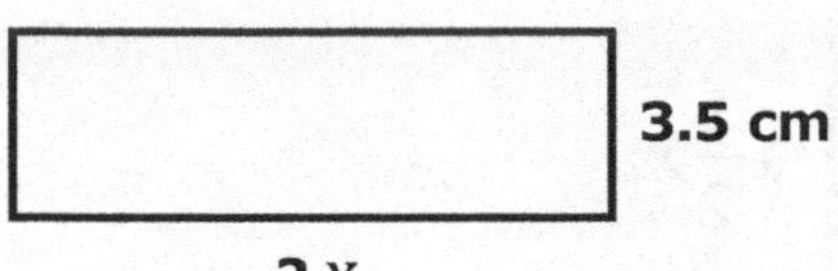

The area of the base is 42 square centimeters and the height of the prism is 1 centimeter shorter than the longest side of the base.

What is the volume of this prism?

A. 105 cubic centimeters
B. 1,470 cubic centimeters
C. 5,053 cubic centimeters
D. 462 cubic centimeters

7.G.B.6

13. This square is the base of a prism.

The volume of this prism is 81 in^3. Which picture represents this prism?

A.

3 in.
3 in.
3 in.

B.

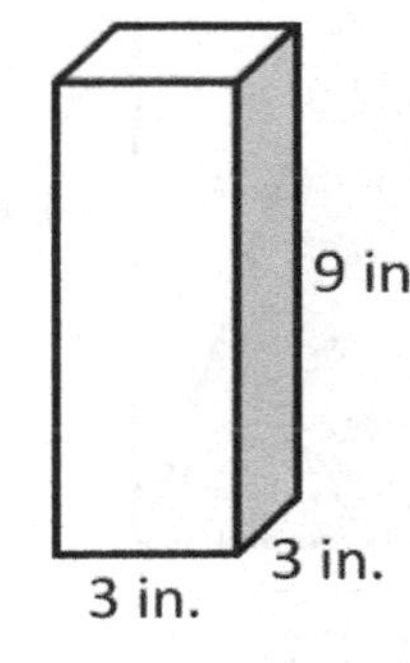

C.

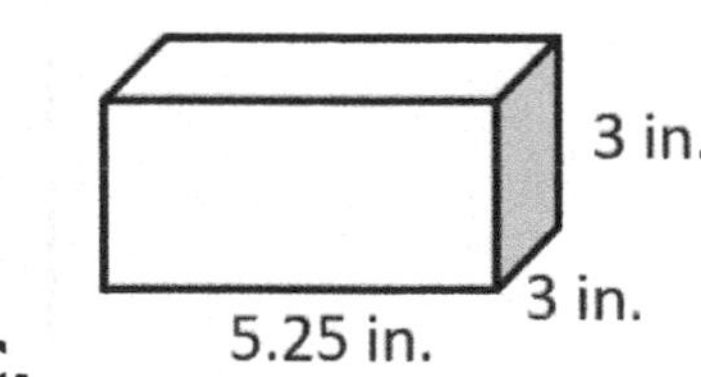

D.

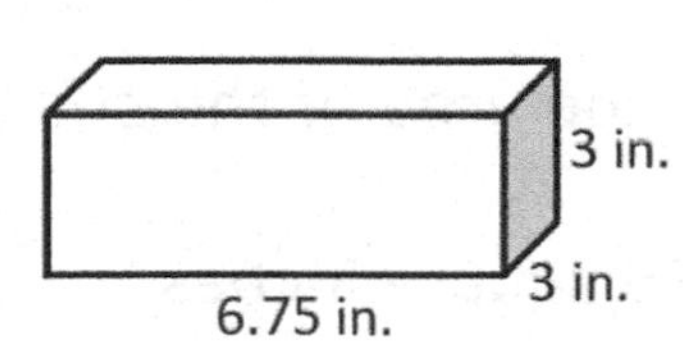

7.G.B.6

14. Which expression can be used to determine the volume of this prism?

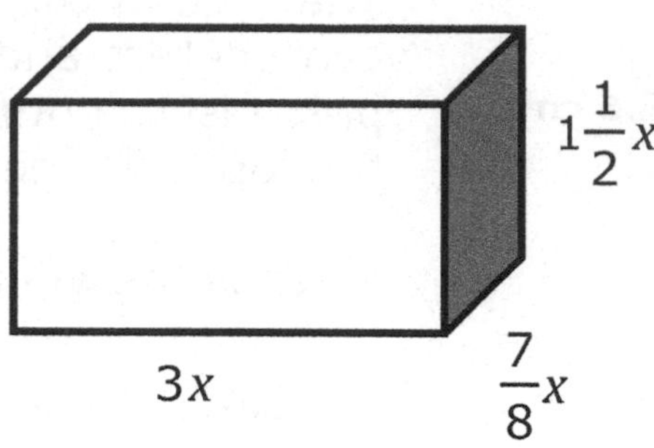

A. $3(3x)(\frac{7}{8}x)(1\frac{1}{2}x)$

B. $(3x)(\frac{7}{8}x)(1\frac{1}{2}x)$

C. $(3x) + (\frac{7}{8}x) + (1\frac{1}{2}x)$

D. $2(3x)(\frac{7}{8}x) + 2(1\frac{1}{2}x)(3x) + 2(\frac{7}{8}x)(1\frac{1}{2}x)$

7.G.B.6

15. Lorraine wants to paint the shaded part of this picture.

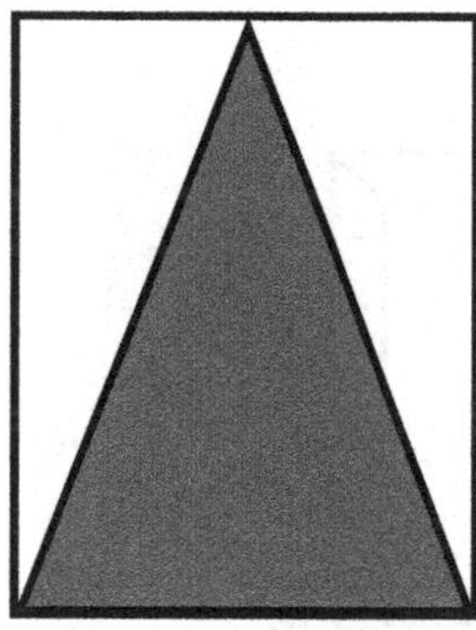

What is the area of the shaded part?

A. 24.75 square inches

B. 40 square inches

C. 49.5 square inches

D. 99 square inches

7.G.B.6

16. How does the volume of Prism A compare to the volume of Prism B?

Prism A

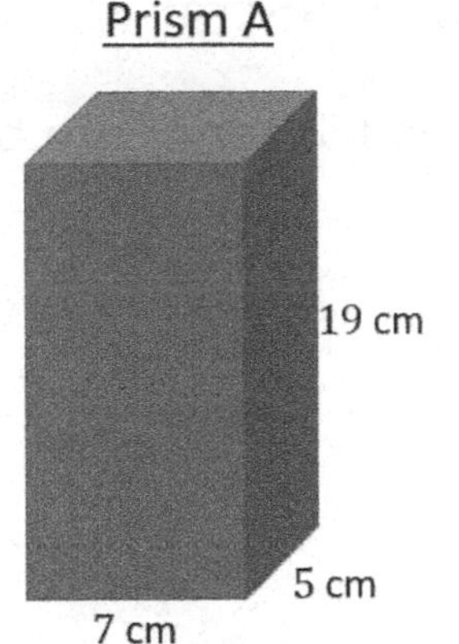

Prism B

10 cm
7 cm
14 cm

A. The volume of Prism A is greater than the volume of Prism B.

B. The volume of Prism B is greater than the volume of Prism A

C. The volume of Prism A is equal to the volume of Prism B.

D. The volume of Prism B is 7 cubic centimeters less than the volume of Prism A.

(7.G.B.6)

17. Which polygon has a larger area?

Polygon A: 3 sides, base length – 6 inches, height – 4 inches

Polygon B: 4 sides, all angles are right angles, length – 5 inches, height 5 inches

____

____

____

(7.G.B.6)

18. Which polygon has a larger area?

Polygon A: A heptagon with an area of $90.85\,\text{cm}^2$

Polygon B: Has 3 sides, with a height of 15.5 cm. The base length is half the height.

____

____

(7.G.B.6)

19. Winston is calculating the volume of this triangular prism.

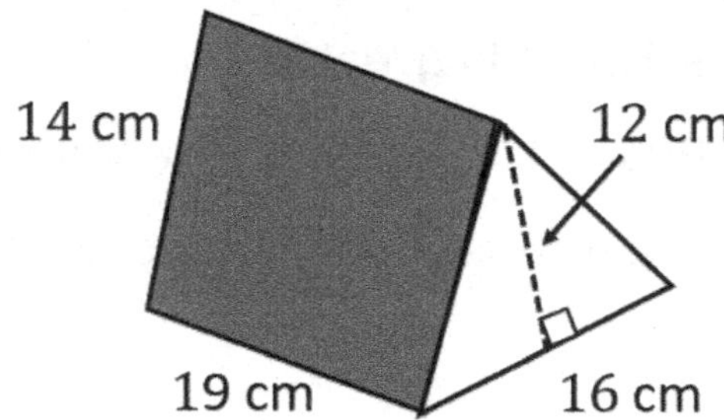

He uses this expression to calculate the volume: $\frac{(16 \times 12)}{2} \times 14$

Do you agree with Winston? Explain your reasoning.

____

____

____

(7.G.B.6)

20. Rebecca is calculating the volume of this prism.

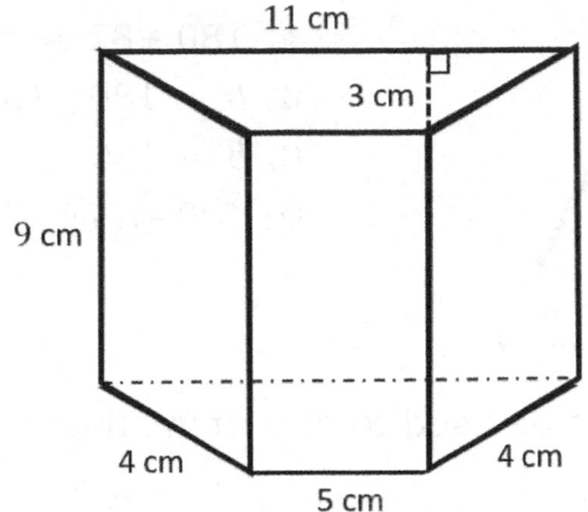

She uses this expression to calculate the volume: $\frac{1}{2}(5+11)(3)\times 9$. Do you agree with Rebecca? Explain your reasoning.

____

____

____

(7.G.B.6)

ANGLE PAIRS

1. Which equation can be used to determine the value of b?

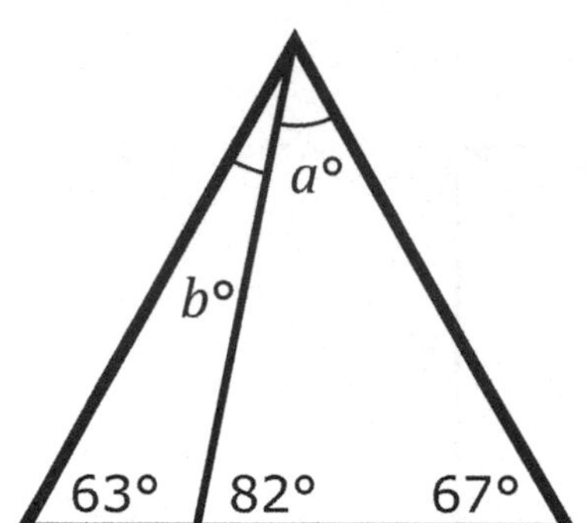

A. $180 - 82 = b$
B. $b = 180 - (82 + 67)$
C. $b = 180 - [180 - (82 + 67)]$
D. $180 - [(180 - 82) + 63] = b$

(7.G.B.5)

2. Which equation can be used to determine the value of a?

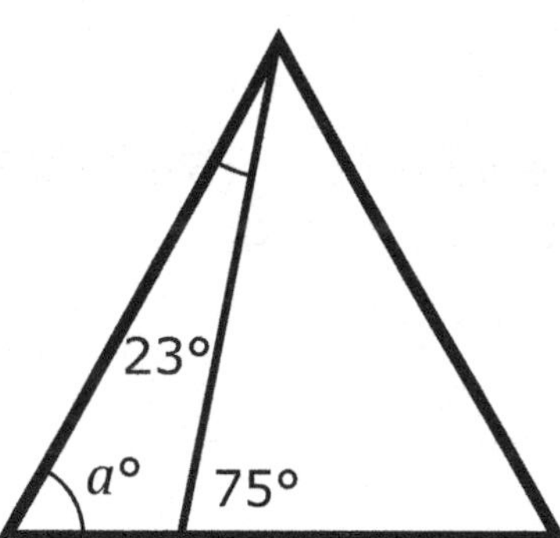

A. $a = 75 + 23$
B. $180 - (75 + 23) = a$
C. $a = 180 - [(180 - 75) + 23]$
D. $(180 - 75) + 23 = a$

(7.G.B.5)

3. The combined values c and d in this graphic is 70°.

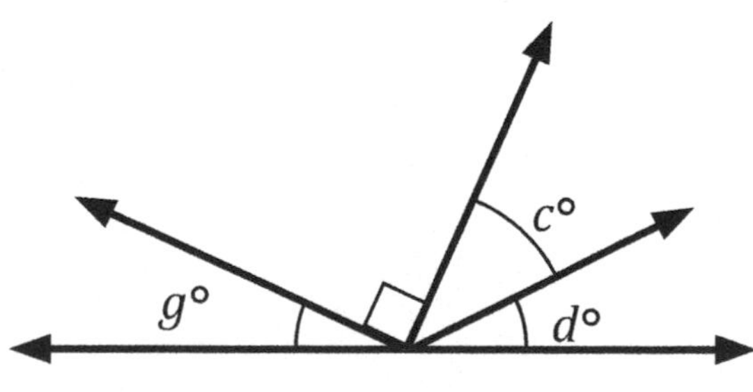

Which equation can be used to find the value of g?

A. $g = 90 - 70$
B. $g = 180 - 70$
C. $g = 90 + 70$
D. $g = 70 + 90 + 180$

(7.G.B.5)

4. Which equation represents the relationship between the three labeled angles in this graphic?

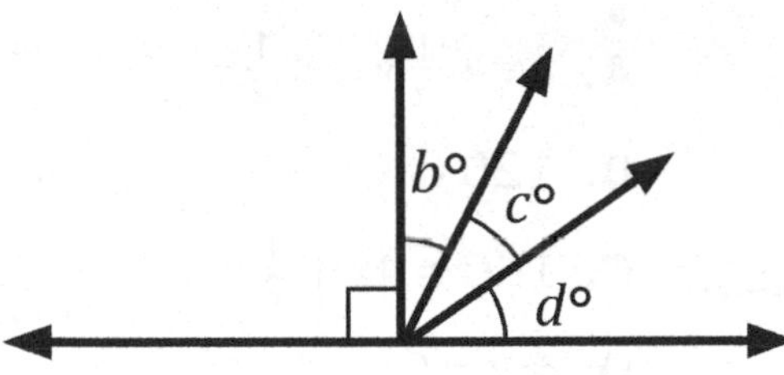

A. $180 = b + c + d$

B. $90 = b + c + d$

C. $0 = 180 - b - c - d$

D. $90 = b - c - d$

(7.G.B.5)

5. Which equation represents the relationship between the vertical angles in this graphic?

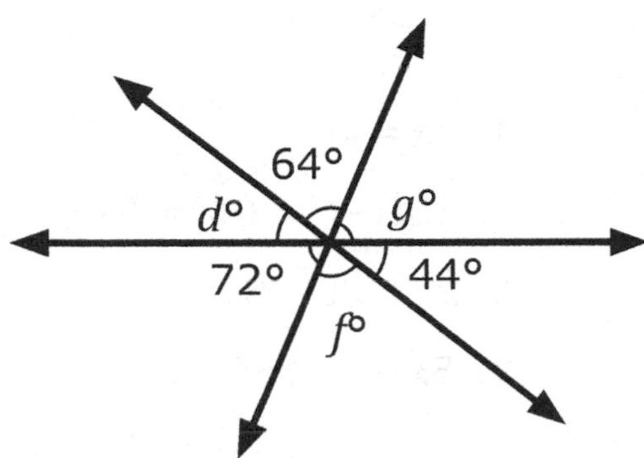

A. $f = 44$

B. $d = 136$

C. $g = 72$

D. $d = 64$

(7.G.B.5)

6. Which equation represents the relationship between the angles in this graphic?

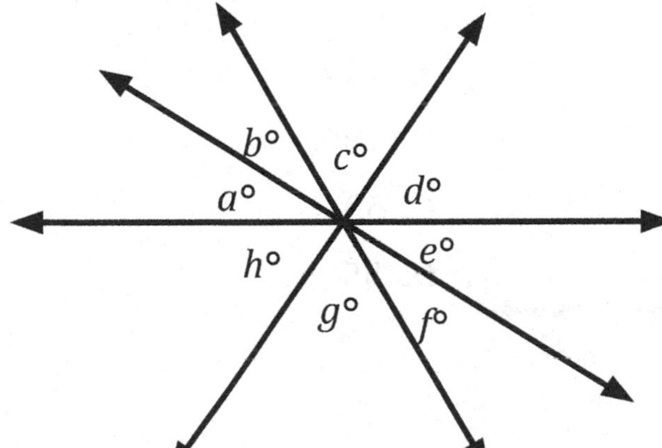

A. $180 = a + f + c + h$

B. $a + b + c = 180$

C. $180 = h + g + c$

D. $a + b + e + f = = 180$

(7.G.B.5)

ANGLE PAIRS

7. Which equation can be used to find the measure of ∠ ABD ?

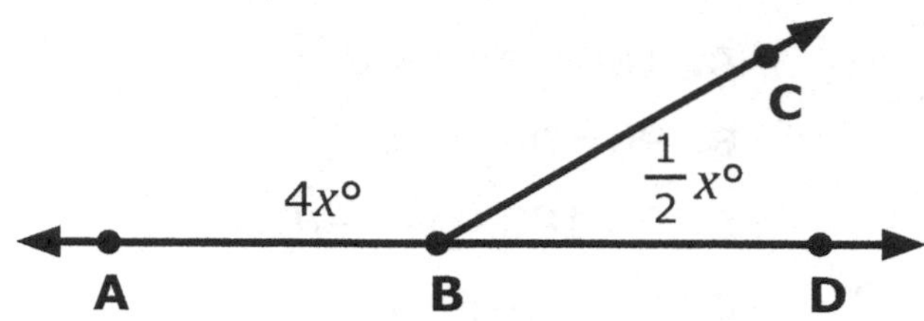

A. $4x+\frac{1}{2}x=4\frac{1}{2}x$

B. $120=4x$

C. $180=4x+\frac{1}{2}x$

D. $\frac{1}{2}x=65$

(7.G.B.5)

8. Which equation can be used to find the measure of ∠ CBD?

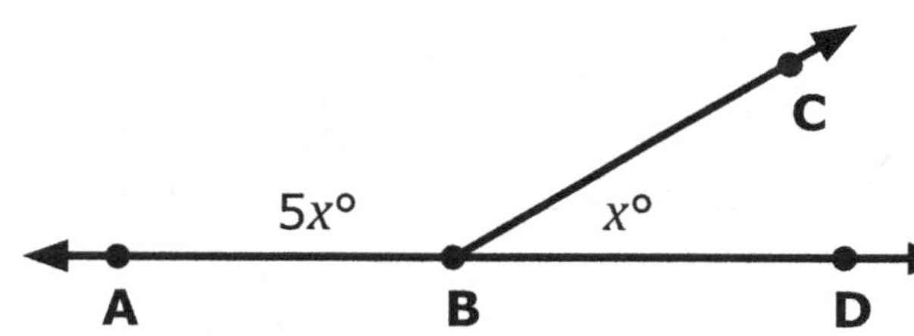

A. $5x=x$

B. $180-(5x+x)=5x$

C. $x=180\div6$

D. $5x-x=150$

(7.G.B.5)

9. What is the measure of ∠ DEF?

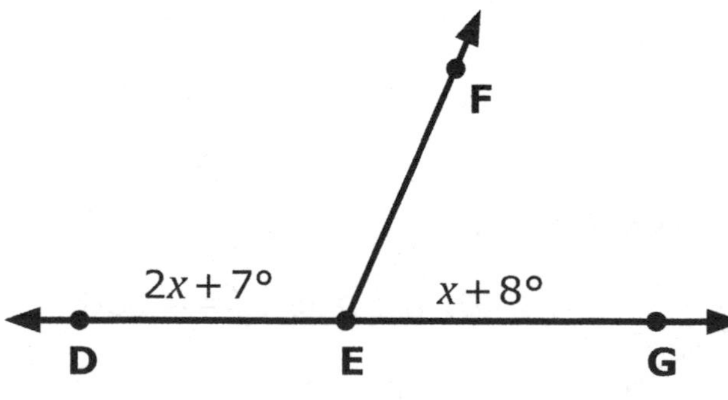

A. 117

B. 180

C. 63

D. 55

(7.G.B.5)

10. Jonah is finding the measure of two angles that are adjacent and supplementary. The measure of one angle is $(4x+9)°$. The measure of the second angle is $(3x-4)°$.

Which graphic represents these two angles?

A.

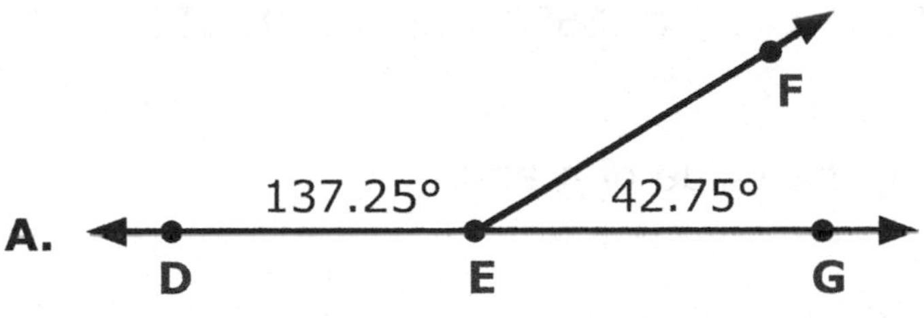

B.

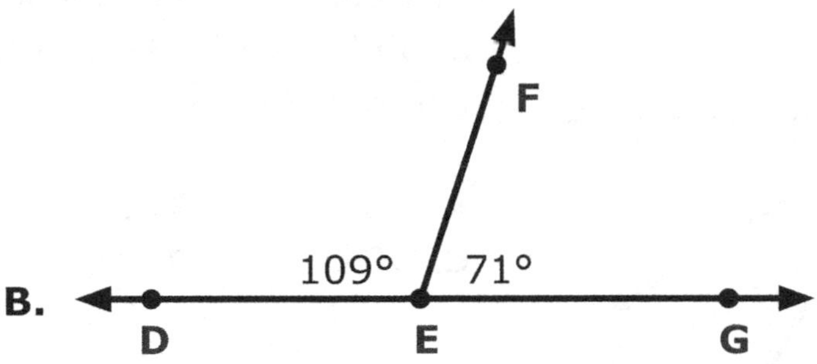

C.

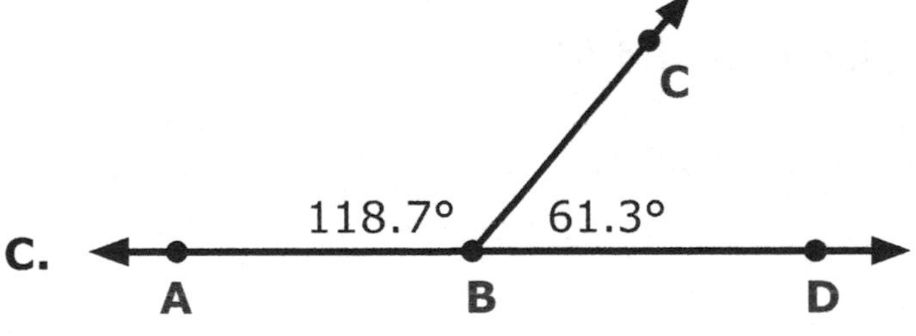

D.

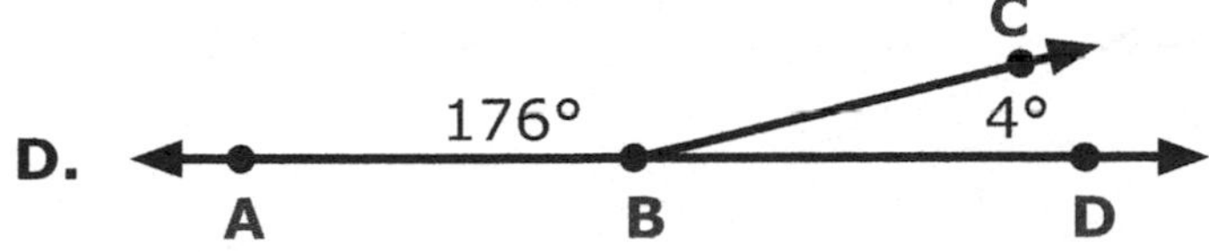

7.G.B.5

ANGLE PAIRS

11. Eli is finding the measure of two angles that are adjacent and supplementary. The measure of one angle is $(9x-20)°$. The measure of the second angle is $(3x+20)°$.

What is the measure of the smallest angle?

A. 90° **B.** 45° **C.** 65° **D.** 15°

(7.G.B.5)

12. Constance is determining the value of a and e.

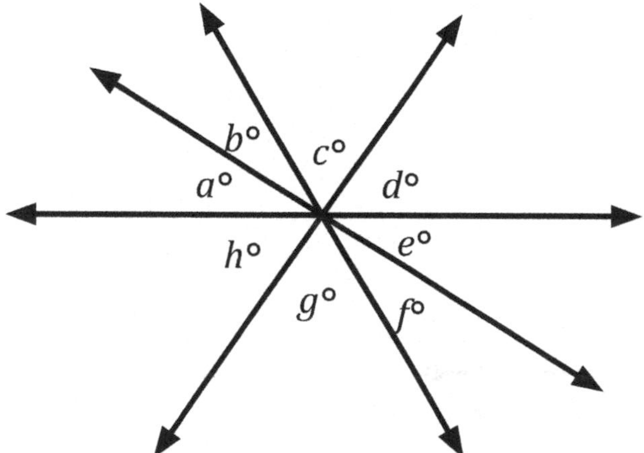

The combined values of b, c, and d is 132. What is the combined values of a and e?

A. 48 **B.** 96
C. 90 **D.** 180

(7.G.B.5)

13. What is the combined value of a and b?

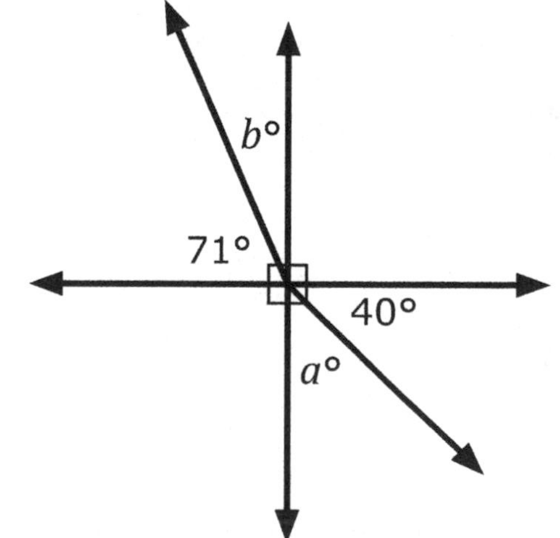

____

(7.G.B.5)

14. What is the combined value of a and b?

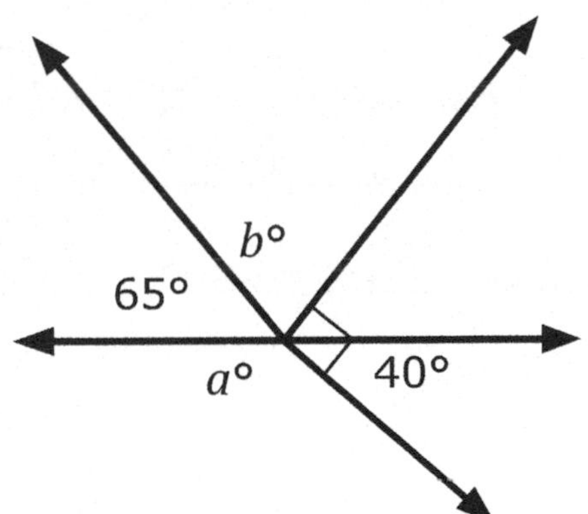

____

(7.G.B.5)

15. What is the value of x?

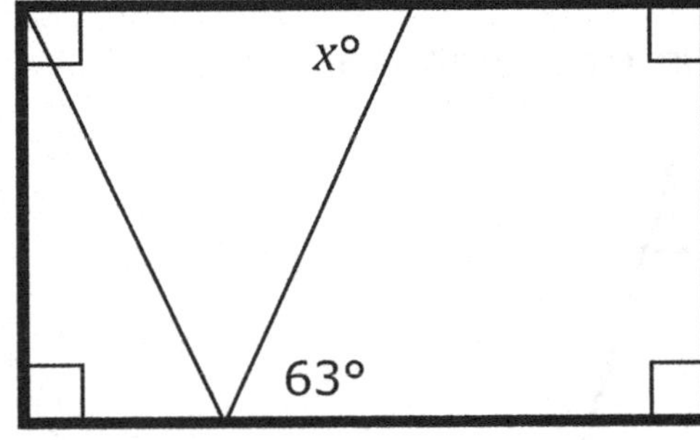

____

____

____

(7.G.B.5)

16. How much larger is a than b?

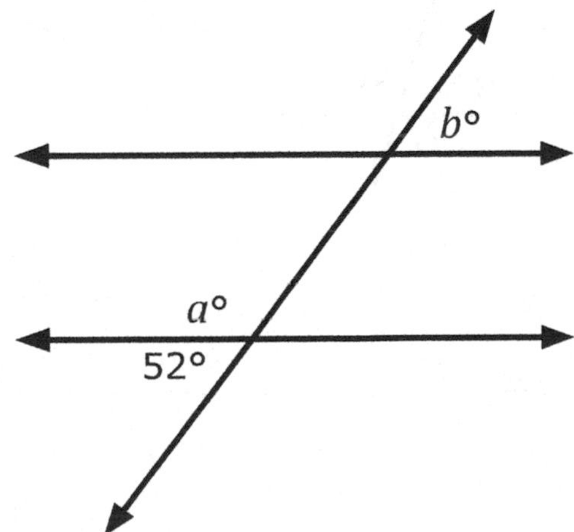

____

____

____

(7.G.B.5)

17. How much larger is z than y?

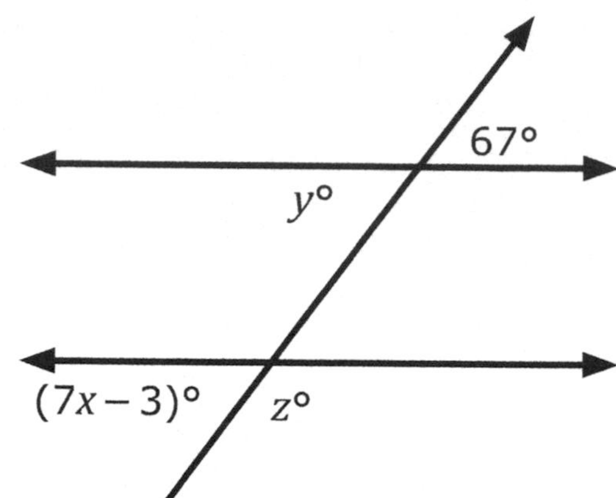

7.G.B.5

18. What is the measure of each angle in trapezoid ABCD?

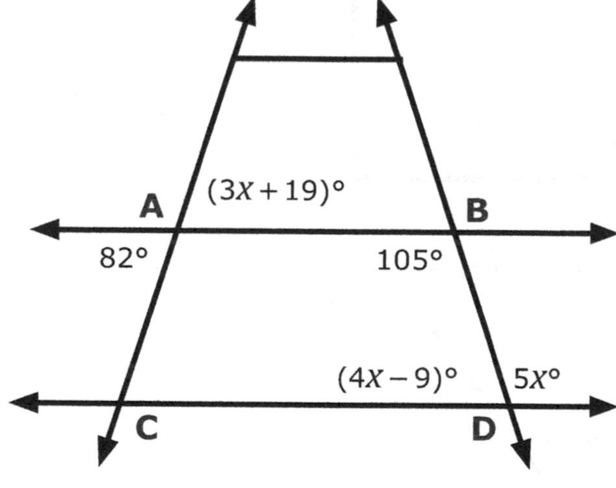

7.G.B.5

19. Is it possible for 2 vertical angles to also be supplementary angles? Explain your reasoning.

____

____

____

(7.G.B.5)

20. Caitlin represents the measure of both $\angle$ ABC and $\angle$ CBD with the expression $4x$.

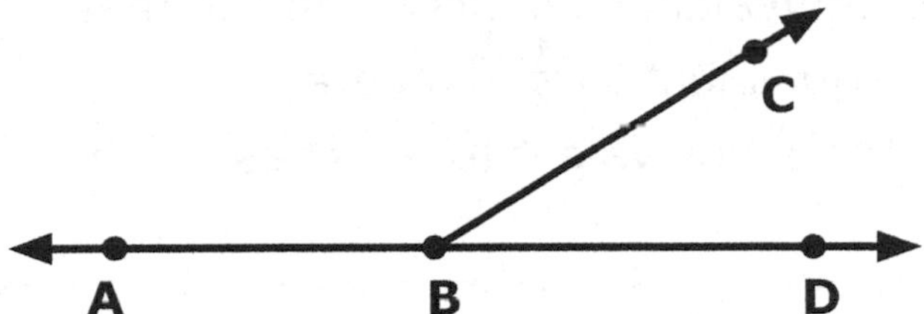

She writes this equation and explanation to determine the measure of each angle:

$$4x + 4x = 180$$

$$8x = 180$$

$$x = 22.5$$

Each angle has a measure of 90 degrees. Do you agree with Caitlin?

____

____

____

(7.G.B.5)

1. Chan Ming draws this scale on a map he is creating.

$\frac{1}{2}$ inch = $\frac{1}{8}$ mile

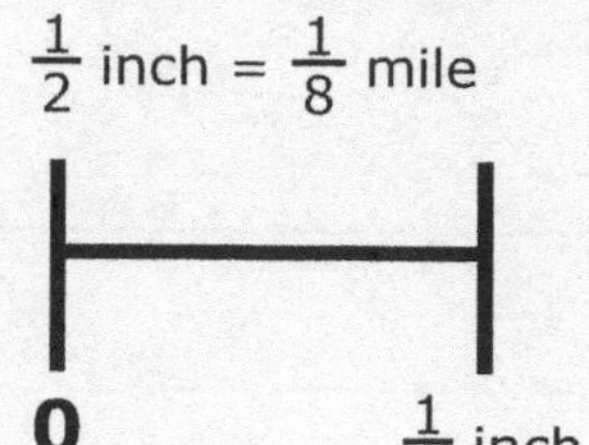

Which statement correctly describes the relationship modeled by the scale?

A. One inch is less than $\frac{1}{4}$ mile.

B. One mile is equivalent to 4 inches on the map.

C. One inch is equivalent to $\frac{1}{2}$ kilometer.

D. One kilometer is equivalent to 3 inches on the map.

(7.G.A.1)

2. Savannah is creating a scale drawing of her house. The scale she creates shows 1 centimeter represents $4\frac{1}{2}$ feet. Savannah's house is 40 feet wide.

What is the width of Savannah's house in the scale drawing?

A. 0.1 cm **B.** 8.9 cm **C.** 7.9 cm **D.** 10 cm

(7.G.A.1)

3. Carole is creating a scale drawing of her classroom. The scale she creates shows 1.5 inches represents 3.75 feet. The length of the classroom is 24 feet.

What is the length of the classroom in Carole's scale drawing?

A. 9 in. **B.** 6.4 in. **C.** 9.6 in. **D.** 16 in.

(7.G.A.1)

4. Which quadrilateral could have these angle measurements?

104°, 27°, 76°, 153°

A. rhombus **B.** kite **C.** trapezoid **D.** rectangle

(7.G.A.2)

5. Which polygon could be created with these characteristics?

- The polygon has 4 sides
- The polygon has angle measurements of 78°,78°,102°,102°

A. rectangle **B.** rhombus **C.** square **D.** kite

(7.G.A.2)

6. Sebastian constructs Triangle ABC. $\overline{AB}$ is 12 inches, and $\overline{CA}$ is 12 inches. The measure of $\angle$ B is 40°.

How many more triangles can Sebastian construct with the same measurements?

A. 1 **B.** 0 **C.** 2 **D.** 3

(7.G.A.2)

7. Brian is using this protractor to construct obtuse isosceles ΔRST.

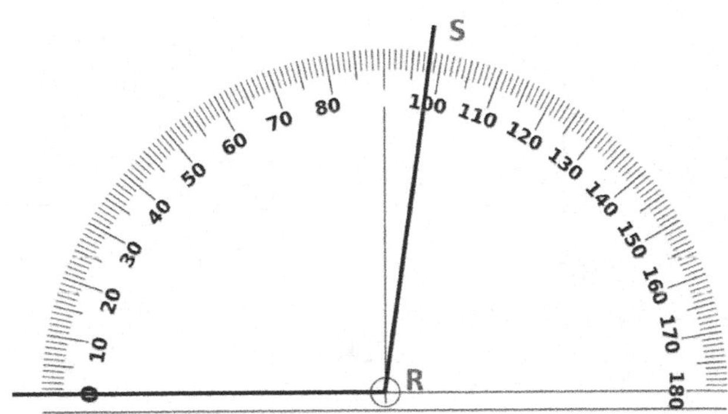

...question 7. continued next page

CHAPTER REVIEW

What is the measure of ∠ S?

____

(7.G.A.2)

8. Which shape is created when a cross section in a cone passes through the cone diagonally to the base, without passing through the base?

A. circle **B.** square **C.** ellipse **D.** rectangle

(7.G.A.3)

9. Which figure shows the cross-section along the diagonal of a prism?

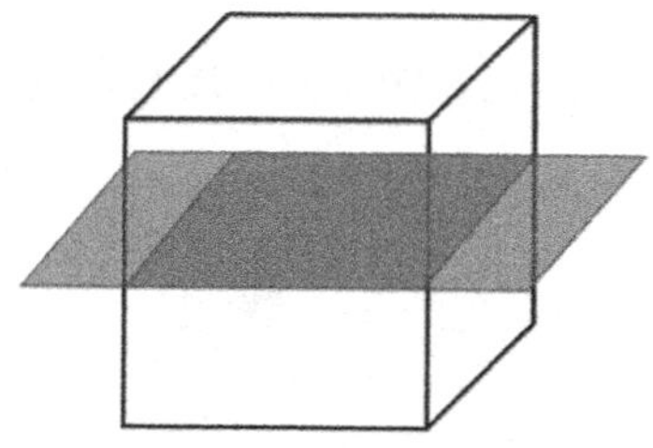

A.

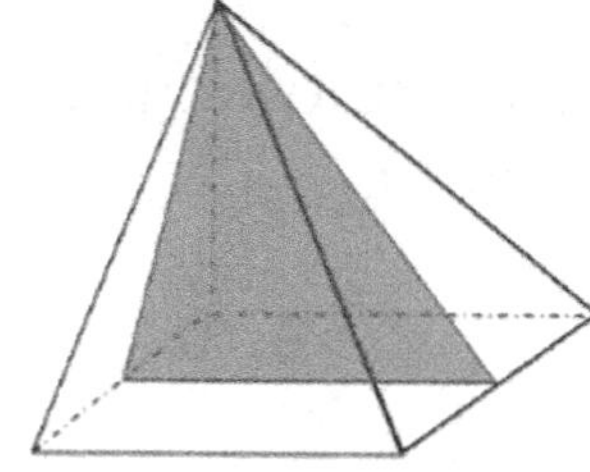

B.

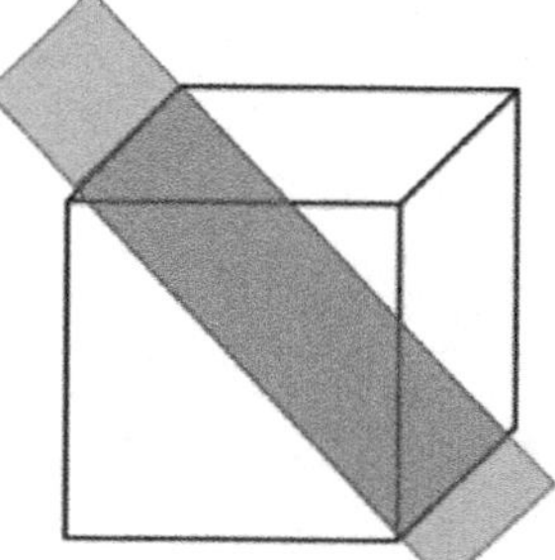

C.

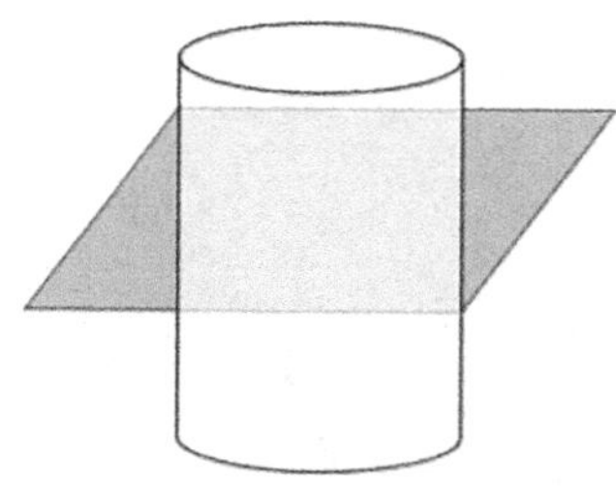

D.

(7.G.A.3)

10. What shape is created by this cross section?

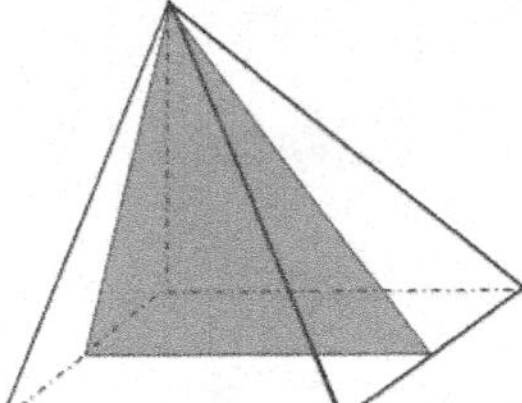

A. triangle **B.** pyramid

C. rectangle **D.** square

(7.G.A.3)

11. Which solid has cross section like the one shown in this drawing when sliced parallel to its base?

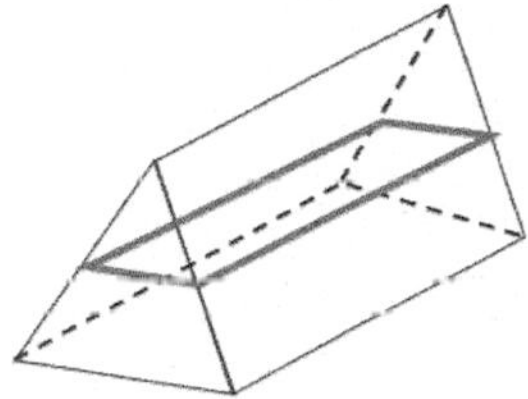

A. triangular prism **B.** cylinder

C. triangular pyramid **D.** rectangular pyramid

(7.G.A.3)

12. A circular watch has a circumference of 16 centimeters. What is the length of the second hand of the watch?

A. 2.55 cm **B.** 5.08 cm **C.** 3.14 cm **D.** 2.31 cm

(7.G.B.4)

13. The tip of the minute hand on this watch rotates at a speed of 1.57 millimeters per minute.

What is the length of the minute hand on this watch?

A. 94.2 mm **B.** 30 mm

C. 15 mm **D.** 4.93 mm

(7.G.B.4)

CHAPTER REVIEW

14. The area of a circle is $\frac{\pi}{16}$ square inches. What is the length of the circle's diameter?

7.G.B.4

15. What is the value of b?

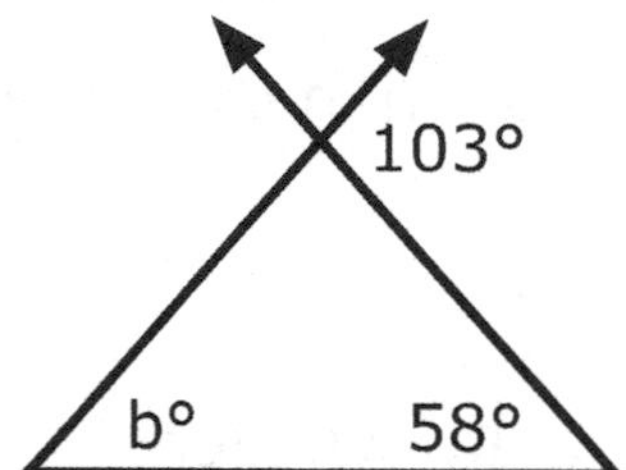

A. 32 **B.** 45
C. 77 **D.** 122

7.G.B.5

16. What is the value of c?

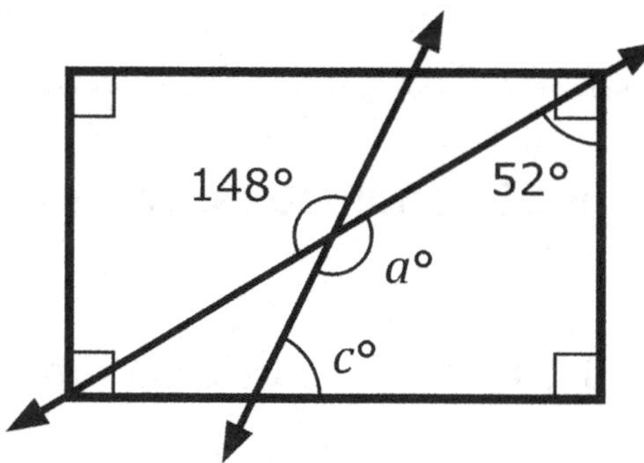

A. 148 **B.** 90
C. 70 **D.** 32

7.G.B.5

17. What is the value of x?

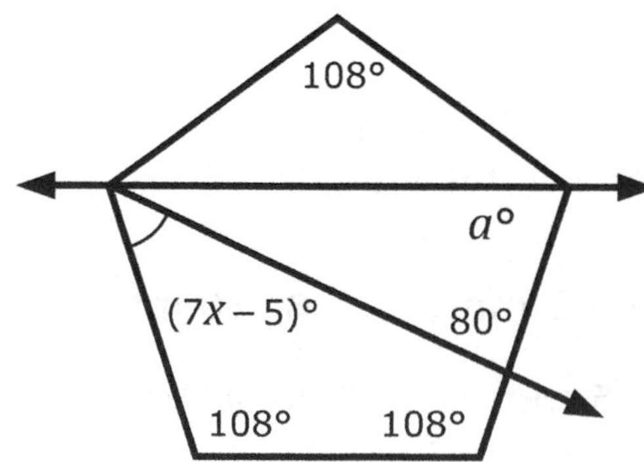

7.G.B.5

18. Milo is painting the shaded part of this picture.

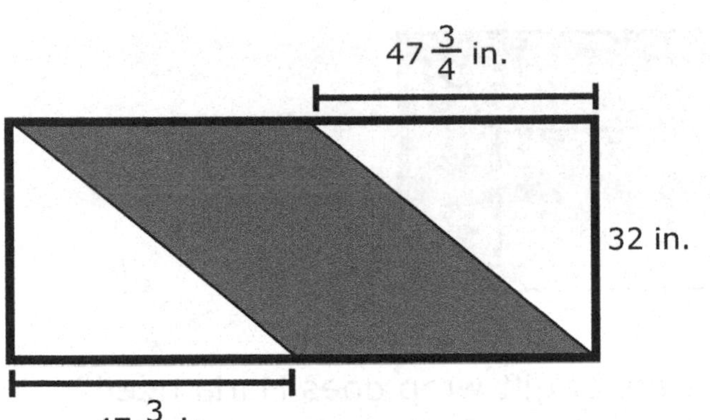

He uses $\frac{1}{2}$ pint of paint for every 100 square inches. Approximately how many pints of paint does Milo need?

A. 30.56

B. 1,528

C. 15.28

D. 61.12

(7.G.B.6)

19. Corrine is painting the bases (ends) of this gift box shaped like a triangular prism.

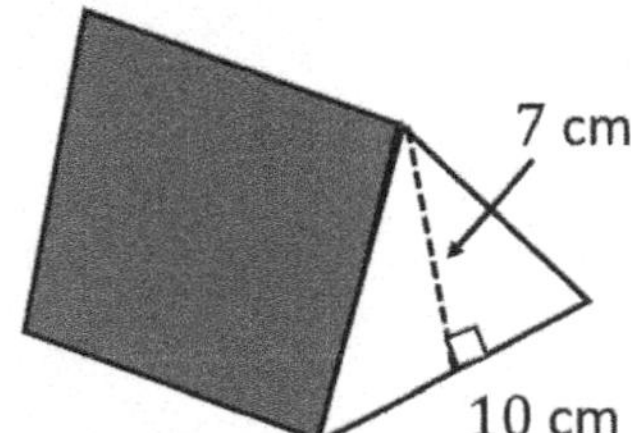

She uses 25 milliliters of paint to cover every 10 square centimeters.

Which statement explains why Corrine uses 175 milliliters of paint to cover the bases of this gift box?

A. The triangular prism has 5 faces.

B. The area of one base is 70 square centimeters.

C. The area of both bases is 70 square centimeters.

D. Corrine paints less than half of the gift box.

(7.G.B.6)

20. Maria is covering this box with gift wrap.

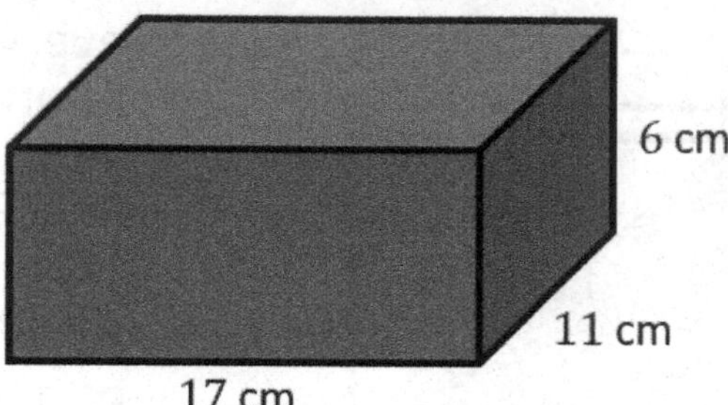

How many square centimeters of gift wrap does Maria need?

____

(7.G.B.6)

1. Ichiro creates a model of the Washington Monument and the United States Capital. Both structures use a scale in which 1 inch to 100 feet.

The Washington Monument, with a height of 555 feet, is almost twice the size of his scale model of the United States Capitol.

Which expression could be used to estimate the height, in inches, of Ichiro's model of the United States Capitol?

A. $2(555)$ **B.** $\left(\frac{555}{2}\right) \div 100$ **C.** $\frac{555}{2}$ **D.** $2\left(\frac{555}{100}\right)$

(7.G.A.1)

2. Teresa draws a regular hexagon with a perimeter of 42 inches. She then draws a similar hexagon with a perimeter of 63 inches.

What scale factor did she use to create the larger hexagon?

____

(7.G.A.1)

3. Idina uses this scale to draw a map of the Yangtze River.

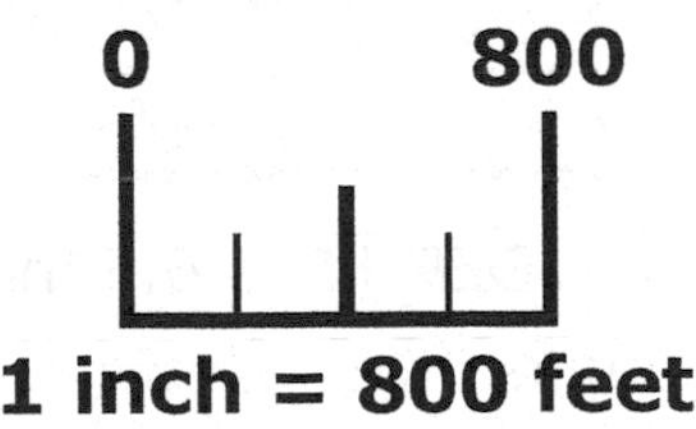

The actual length of the Yangtze River is 3,915 miles. She estimates the length of the river on her map will be approximately 50 inches.

...question 3. continued next page

EXTRA PRACTICE

Do you agree with Idina? Explain your reasoning.

____

____

____

7.G.A.1

4. Mark is constructing a triangle. The length of two sides are 12 inches and 10 centimeters.

Which length could represent the third side of Mark's triangle?

A. 28 **B.** 24 **C.** 14 **D.** 2

7.G.A.2

5. Debra constructs Triangle ABC. $\overline{AB}$ is 9 inches, $\overline{CA}$ is 13 inches, and $\angle A$ has a measure of 28°.

How many more triangles can Debra construct with the same measurements?

A. 1 **B.** 0 **C.** 2 **D.** 3

7.G.A.2

6. Gaura constructs Triangle DEF. $\overline{FE}$ is 6.5 inches, $\overline{FD}$ is 8.4 inches, and $\angle$ F is an obtuse angle.

Which measurement could represent the measure of $\angle D$?

A. 120 **B.** 78 **C.** 68 **D.** 33

7.G.A.2

7. Lelita believes it is impossible to construct a triangle with side lengths of 3 centimeters, 5 centimeters, and 9 centimeters.

Do you agree with Lelita? Explain your reasoning.

____

____

____

7.G.A.2

8. Which statement is true?

A. The cross section of a hexagonal prism parallel to its base is a hexagon.

B. The cross section of every prism is a rectangle.

C. The cross section of a triangular prism is always a triangle.

D. The cross section of a square pyramid is a square.

7.G.A.3

9. Which statement is true?

A. A rectangle is formed when a pentagonal prism is sliced perpendicularly to its base.

B. An octagon is formed when a 10-sided prism is sliced parallel to its base.

C. The cross section of any pyramid is a triangle.

D. The cross section of any prism is a rectangle.

7.G.A.3

10. Amelia creates a cross section by slicing a triangular pyramid perpendicular to its base. Which shape does she create?

A.  **B.** **C.**  **D.** 

(7.G.A.3)

11. Niran slices this three-dimensional solid vertically from Point A to Point B.

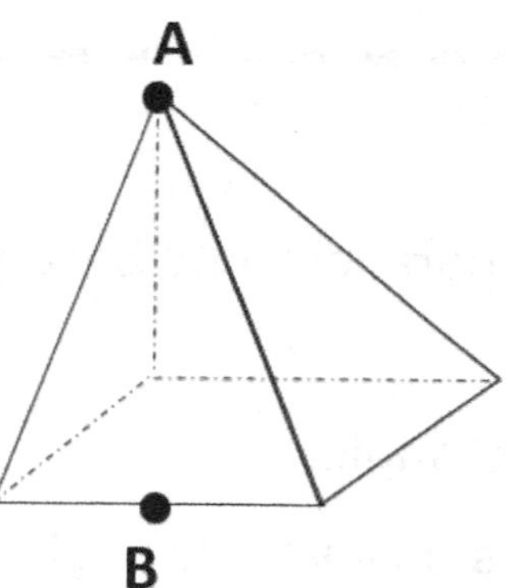

Which shape does Niran create?

____

(7.G.A.3)

12. The circumference of a quarter is 75 millimeters and a height of 1.75 mm. What is the maximum number of quarters that can fit inside this collector's case?

Coin Collector Case

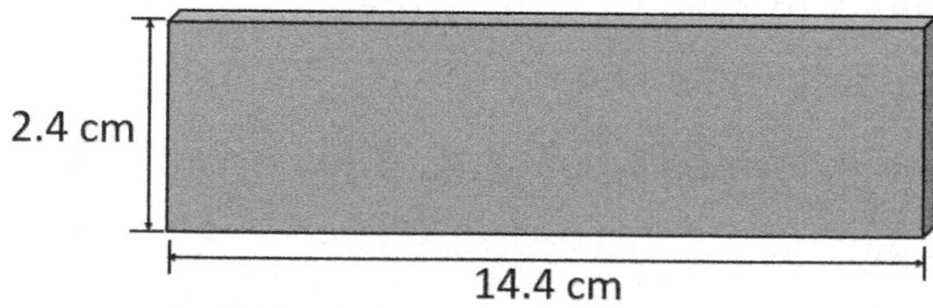

A. 82 **B.** 100 **C.** 50 **D.** 74

(7.G.B.4)

13. Pavati wants to hang a circular clock, at the center of the wall, along the horizontal line shown on this wall.

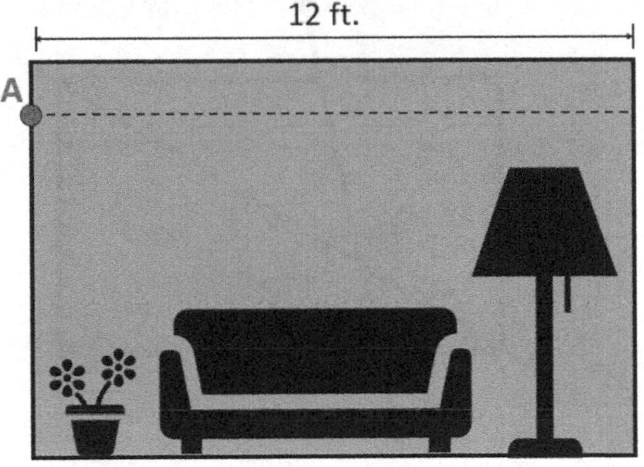

The clock has a circumference of 75.36 inches. What is the distance between Point A and the edge of the clock?

A. 72 in. **B.** 60 in. **C.** 24 in. **D.** 12 in.

(7.G.B.4)

14. Umar uses this web camera with his 15-inch computer.

The diameter of the web camera is $\frac{1}{12}$ the width of his computer.

What is the circumference of the web camera?

____

(7.G.B.4)

15. Which equation can be used to determine the value of a?

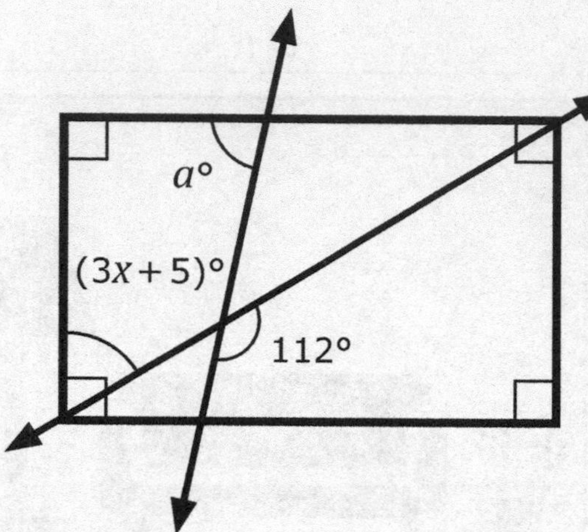

A. $a = 112 + x$
B. $a = 90 + (3x + 5)$
C. $a = 180 - (3x + 5) - 112$
D. $a = 360 - (3x + 5) - 90 - 112$

7.G.B.5

16. What is the value of a?

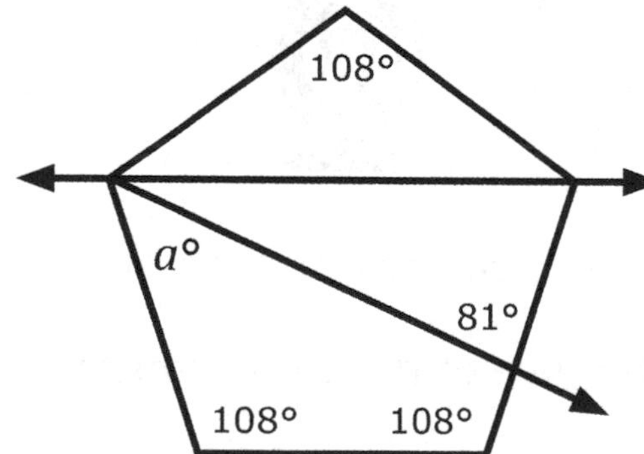

______

7.G.B.5

EXTRA PRACTICE

17. What is the value of x? Show your work.

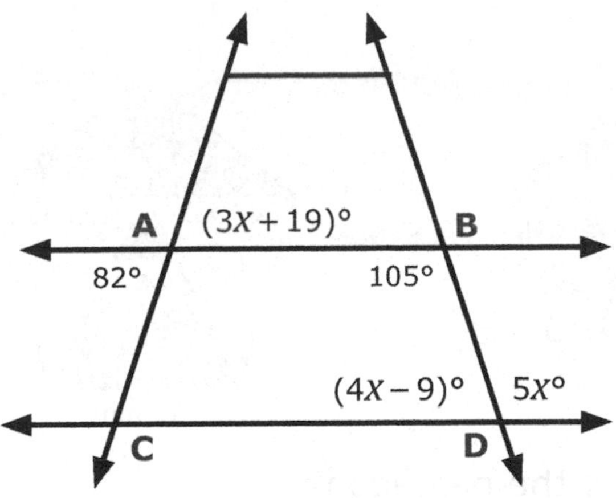

____

____

____

7.G.B.5

18. John states that the volume of a rectangular prism is 1,728 in^3. If the rectangular prism is a cube, what is the length of each side?

____

7.G.B.6

19. Samantha fills this prism halfway with candy.

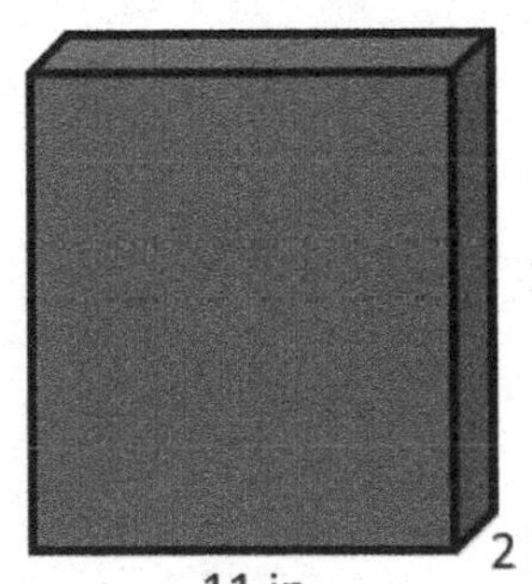

What is the volume of the candy in the prism?

A. 175 cubic inches **B.** 349 cubic inches

C. 143 cubic inches **D.** 286 cubic inches

7.G.B.6

EXTRA PRACTICE

20. Gary determines the area of this pentagon by decomposing it into triangles.

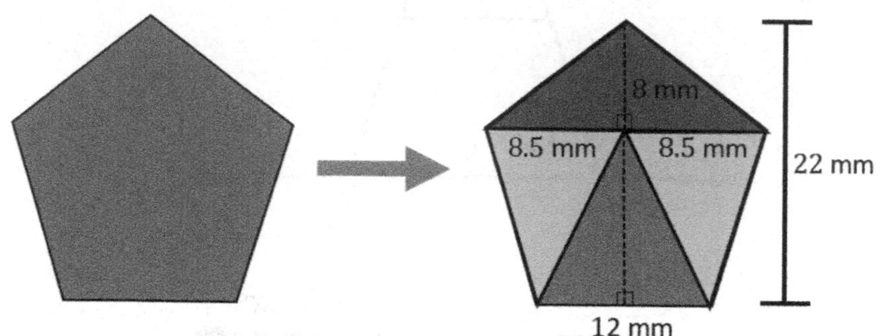

What is the area of the pentagon?

A. 542 mm² **B.** 339 mm² **C.** 271 mm² **D.** 187 mm²

7.G.B.6

STATISTICS AND PROBABILITY

UNDERSTANDING RANDOM SAMPLING	153
COMPARE AND INFER TWO POPULATIONS	163
PROBABILITY MODELS	179
CHAPTER REVIEW	186
EXTRA PRACTICE	194

1. A team of individuals conduct a survey of 400 sixth grade students. They ask each student to respond to this question: "Recycling helps extend the use of the earth's resources. Do you think the school should start a recycling program?"

Will the results of the survey provide valid information about whether the students think the school should start a recycling program?

A. Yes. The students answers will be tallied to provide the required information for the survey results.

B. No. Most 6th grade students are not concerned about the earth's finite resources.

C. Yes. Most 6th grade students are very concerned about the earth's finite resources.

D. No. The question immediately creates bias because it encourages the students to support a recycling program.

(7.SP.A.1)

2. Each day, 1,500 people attend the movies. More men attend the movies than both women and children.

A survey is being conducted to determine which new snack the movie theatre should add to their menu. Which sample would be biased for surveying all the people at the movies?

A. 25 women, 25 men, 25 children

B. 20 women, 50 men, 30 children

C. 60 women, 10 men, 5 children

D. 10 women, 10 men, 20 children

(7.SP.A.1)

UNDERSTANDING RANDOM SAMPLING

3. Tiana is collecting data about the number of police officers in each city across America.

Which response describes a representative sample for Tiana's data?

A. 40 city police departments from the state she lives in

B. 20 city police departments from each state

C. 1 city police department from each state

D. 30 city police departments from 5 different states

(7.SP.A.1)

4. There are 600 students in Erica's school. Forty-eight percent of the students are boys, and the rest are girls.

Erica collects data from a random sample of students who are representative of the students in her school.

Which response correctly describes the randomness of Erica's sample?

A. Erica surveys 5 boys and 5 girls from her 1st period class.

B. Erica surveys all 600 boys and girls in her school.

C. Erica surveys the first 50 boys and 50 girls she sees at school.

D. Erica surveys 50 boys in the 7th grade, and 100 girls in the 8th grade.

(7.SP.A.1)

5. Evan creates this graph to represent the data he collects from a sample of students in his school.

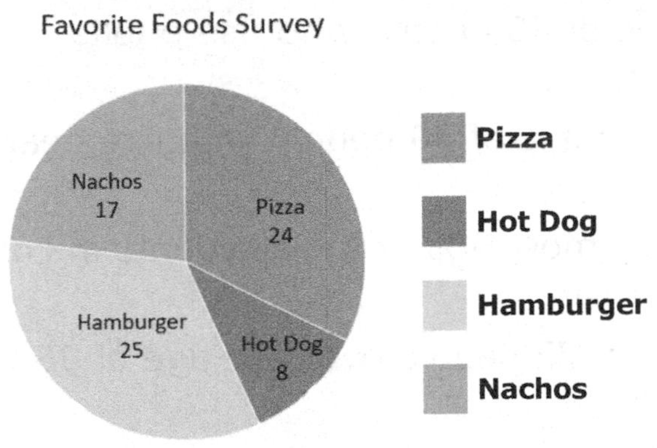

This data is representative of the 550 students in Evan's school.

Based on Evan's survey results, which number approximates how many of the students in the school like hot dogs?

A. 60 **B.** 74 **C.** 250 **D.** 542

7.SP.A.1

6. Linh creates this graph to represent the data she collects from a sample of students in her school.

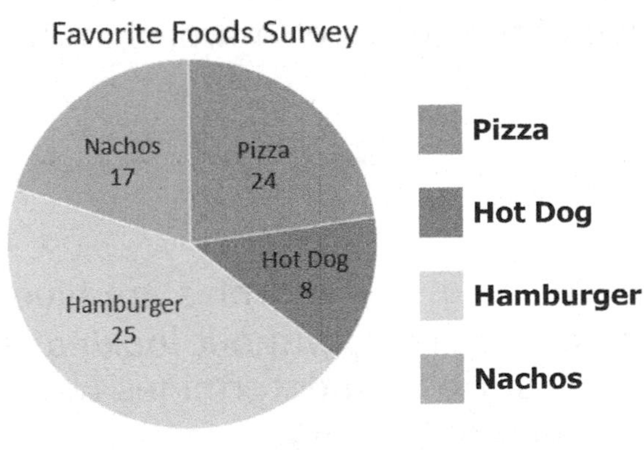

This data is representative of the 360 students in Linh's school.

Based on Linh's survey results, which number best approximates the number of students in the school who like nachos or hamburgers?

A. 318 **B.** 100 **C.** 205 **D.** 42

7.SP.A.1

UNDERSTANDING RANDOM SAMPLING

7. Tomas is summarizing data about the city of Los Angeles. Which survey could describe the entire population of Los Angeles?

A. In a study using a sample of 45 people who use public transportation in Los Angeles.

B. A survey is done with a sample of 70 people who live near a beach.

C. A survey that found that almost 9% of the residents in Los Angeles are African-American.

D. A survey using a sample of 72 people over the age of 35 who responded to a poll.

(7.SP.A.1)

8. Aki places 100 marbles inside a bag. The marbles are blue, black, green, and red.

He draws 20 marbles out of the bag; 9 black marbles, 4 blue marbles, 5 red marbles, and 2 green marbles. He determines approximately 10 % of the marbles in the bag are green.

Is Aki's sample representative of the colors of marbles in the bag?

____

(7.SP.A.1)

9. Xavier places 40 marbles inside a bag. The marbles are blue and black. He reaches inside the bag 10 times, without looking, and draws 3 blue and 7 black marbles. He then determines there are 12 blue marbles and 28 black marbles in the bag.

Is Xavier's sample of marbles biased?

____

(7.SP.A.1)

10. Samir wants to know the average height of the seventh-grade students in his school. There are 175 girls and 182 boys in the seventh grade. He surveys 35 boys and 55 girls.

Is Samir's sample size reasonable based on population of seventh grade students?

____

7.SP.A.1

11. Dev wants to know how many times the word "the" appears in an article he is reading. He counts the number of times "the" appears in one paragraph.

Dev discovers the word appears 13 times in one paragraph, and the article contains 21 paragraphs.

Based on Dev's sample, approximately how many times does the word "the" appear in the entire article?

A. 35 **B.** 270 **C.** 100 **D.** 130

7.SP.A.2

12. Myra wants to determine the average word length in a book she is reading. She counts the length of each word on one page and creates this table.

Word Length	2	3	4	5	6	7	8	9
Number of Occurrences	12	18	75	37	45	19	7	3

Approximately what percent of the book contains words with 5 or more letters?

A. 51 **B.** 105 **C.** 37 **D.** 111

7.SP.A.2

13. Feng wants to determine the average word length in a book he is reading. He counts the length of each word on one page and creates this table.

Word Length	2	3	4	5	6	7	8	9
Number of Occurrences	20	15	64	71	51	25	9	1

Approximately what percent of the book contains words with 4 letters?

A. 13% **B.** 64% **C.** 36% **D.** 25%

(7.SP.A.2)

14. Diego designs 3 surveys to determine the favorite colors of the students in his school. The results of his surveys are in this table.

Survey	**Number of People Surveyed**	**Favorite Colors**			
		Red	**Blue**	**Green**	**Yellow**
A	28	9	4	5	7
B	35	11	5	10	9
C	31	10	4	9	8

There are 400 students in Xavier's school. Based on this data, which color will approximately $\frac{1}{4}$ of the students in Xavier's school select as their favorite?

____

____

____

(7.SP.A.2)

15. Fredo collected data about a group of travelers' recent visit to Morocco. He recorded his data in this table.

Level of Satisfaction with Visit	Number of People
1 – Unsatisfied	2
2 – Somewhat satisfied	5
3 – Satisfied	8
4 – Very satisfied	9

Which generalization could Fredo make based on this data?

A. At least 20% of the travelers were unsatisfied with their visit.

B. More than 90% of the travelers were very satisfied with their visit.

C. More than half of the travelers were satisfied or very satisfied with their visit.

D. Over $\frac{3}{4}$ of the travelers were either unsatisfied or somewhat satisfied with their visit.

(7.SP.A.2)

16. Bomi collected data about a group of travelers' recent visit to Puerto Rico. He recorded his data in this table.

Level of Satisfaction with Visit	Number of People
1 – Unsatisfied	1
2 – Somewhat satisfied	2
3 – Satisfied	5
4 – Very satisfied	4

...question 16. continued next page

Which generalization could Bomi make based on this data?

A. Most people will be satisfied or very satisfied with their visit to Puerto Rico.

B. Less than half of the people visiting Puerto Rico will be satisfied or very satisfied with their visit.

C. Most of the people visiting Puerto Rico will be somewhat satisfied.

D. Less than 1% of people planning to visit Puerto Rico will be unsatisfied.

(7.SP.A.2)

17. Sergio collected data about a group of travelers' recent visit to India. He recorded his data in this table.

Level of Satisfaction with Visit	Number of People
1 – Unsatisfied	2
2 – Somewhat satisfied	7
3 – Satisfied	10
4 – Very satisfied	17

Which generalization could Sergio make based on this data?

A. About 75% of people traveling to India will be very satisfied with their visit.

B. Approximately 27% of people traveling to India will be satisfied or very satisfied with their visit.

C. Less than 2% of people traveling to India will be unsatisfied with their visit.

D. Over 30% of people traveling to India will be unsatisfied or somewhat satisfied with their visit.

(7.SP.A.2)

18. Diego designed 3 surveys to determine the favorite colors of the students in his school. The results of his surveys are in this table.

Survey	Number of People Surveyed	Favorite Colors			
		Red	Blue	Green	Yellow
A	50	30	12	5	3
B	45	27	12	5	1
C	60	36	15	6	3

There are 1,000 students in Diego's school. Approximately how many will prefer green or yellow?

____

(7.SP.A.2)

19. Perry buys a bag of blue, red, and green marbles. He draws 10 marbles from the bag. This table shows his results.

Marble Color	Occurrences (Percent)
Blue	60
Red	30
Green	10

Which list shows a reasonable number of blue, red, and green marbles in the entire bag?

A. Blue marbles – 200
Red marbles – 200
Green marbles – 200

B. Blue marbles – 240
Red marbles – 120
Green marbles – 40

C. Blue marbles – 100
Red marbles – 300
Green marbles – 600

D. Blue marbles – 50
Red marbles – 40
Green marbles – 30

(7.SP.A.2)

20. Chin states that recognizes there are 4 prime numbers between 1 and 10. She estimates there will be 400 prime numbers between 1 and 1,000.

Do you agree with Chin? Explain your reasoning.

____

____

____

(7.SP.A.2)

1. Which statement compares the mean height of the players on these football teams?

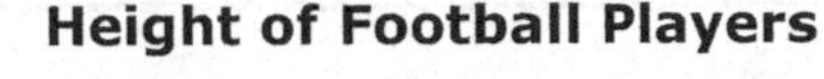

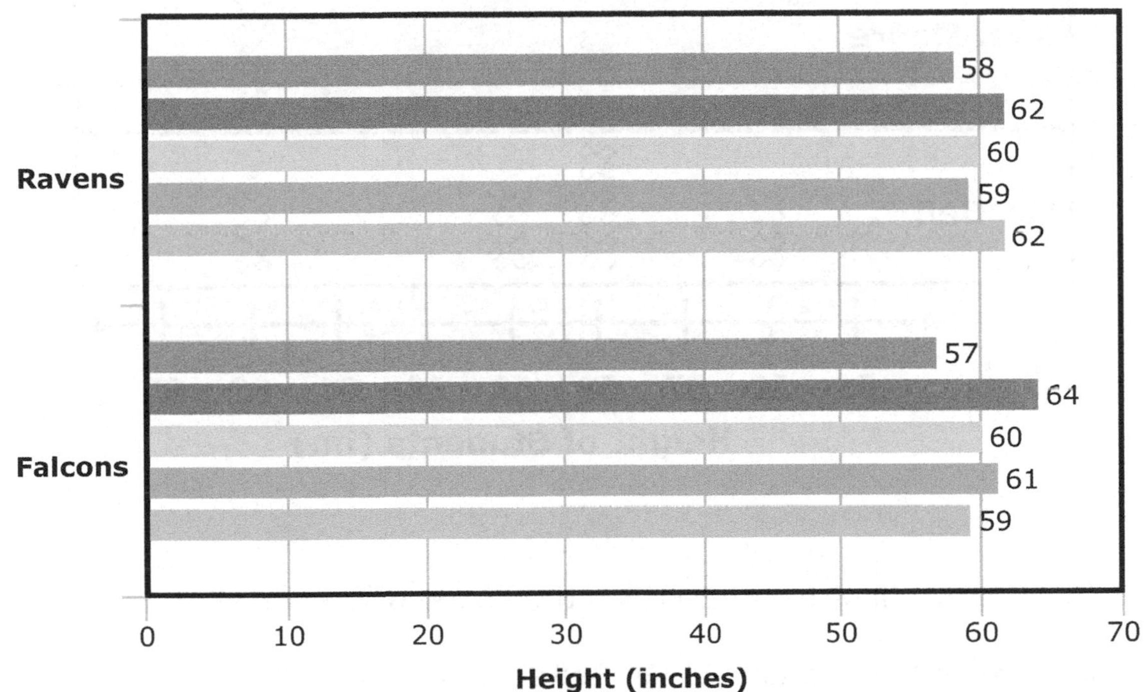

A. The mean height of the Ravens is greater than the mean height of the Falcons.

B. The mean height of both the Ravens and Falcons is 59.

C. The mean height for both football teams is the same.

D. The mean height for the Falcons is 3 more inches than the median.

(7.SP.B.3)

2. This dot plot shows the heights of the students in Mrs. Moore's and Mr. Bell's classes.

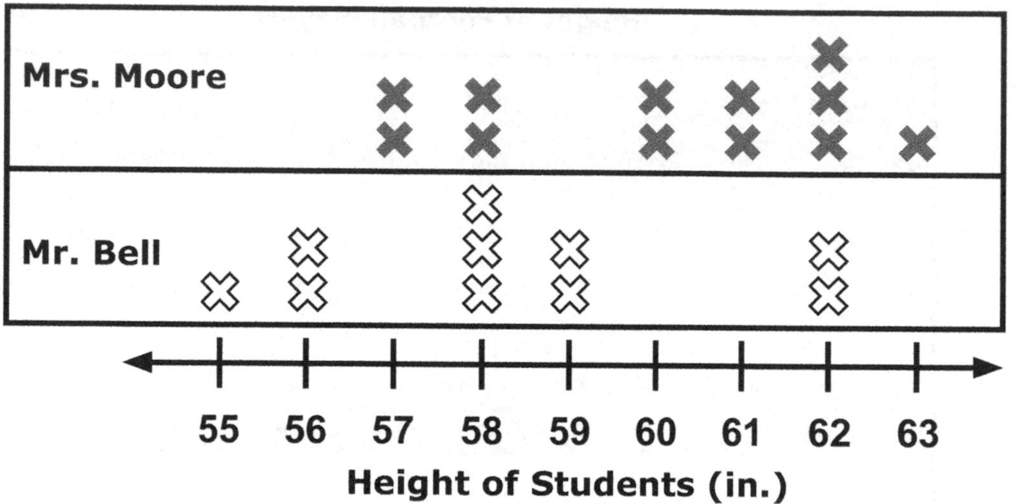

Which statement best describes the shape of the data?

A. Most of the students in Mr. Bell's class are over 59 inches tall.

B. Most of Mrs. Moore's students are shorter than Mr. Bell's students.

C. Most of Mr. Bell's students are shorter than Mrs. Moore's students.

D. More than half of Mrs. Moore's students are over 63 inches tall.

(7.SP.B.3)

3. Which statement describes the mode height of the football players shown on this graph?

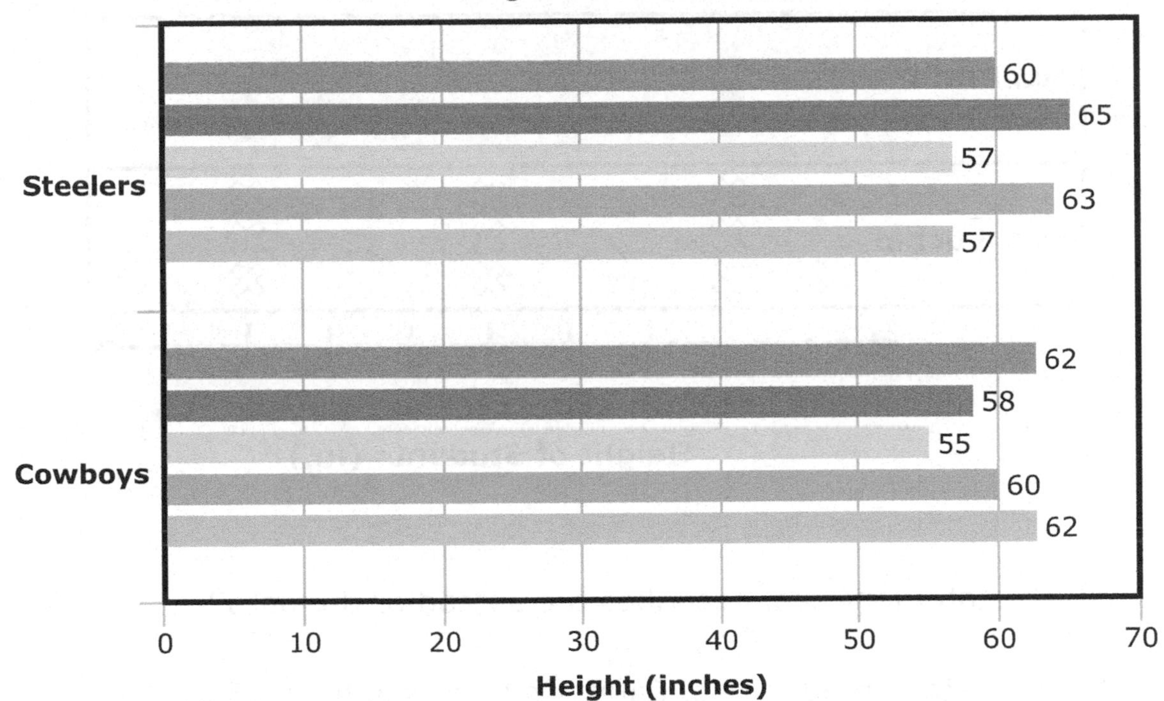

A. The mode height for the Steelers is 57 and the mode height for the Cowboys is 62.

B. The mode height for both teams is 57

C. The mode height for both teams is 62.

D. The mode height for the Steelers is 62 and the mode height for the Cowboys is 57.

(7.SP.B.3)

COMPARE AND INFER TWO POPULATIONS

4. This dot plot shows the heights of the students in Ms. Ratliff's and Mrs. Luchin's classes.

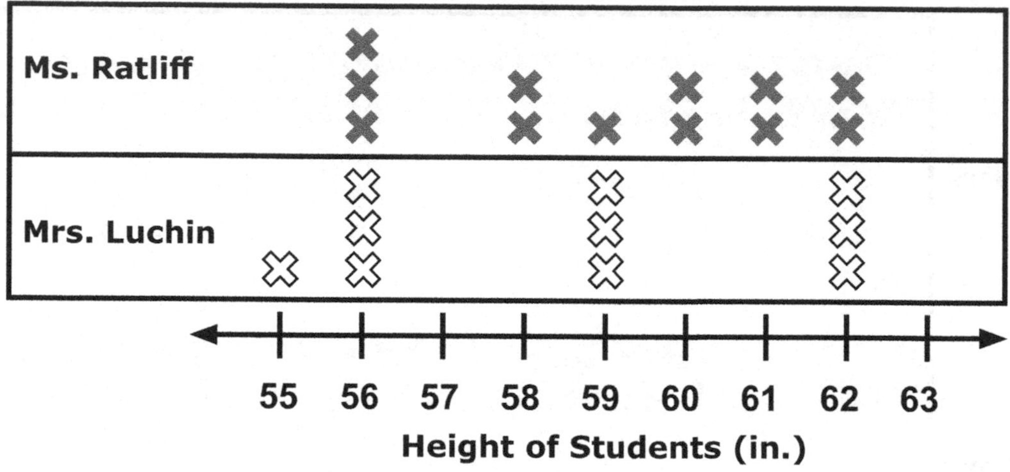

Which statement best describes the spread of the data?

A. The data spread for Ms. Ratliff's students is from 55 inches to 63 inches.

B. The data spread for Mrs. Luchin's students is from 55 inches to 63 inches.

C. There is a greater spread in Ms. Ratliff's data.

D. There is a greater spread in Mrs. Luchin's data.

(7.SP.B.3)

5. The median height of the players on the Steelers is ________ than the height of the players on the Cowboys.

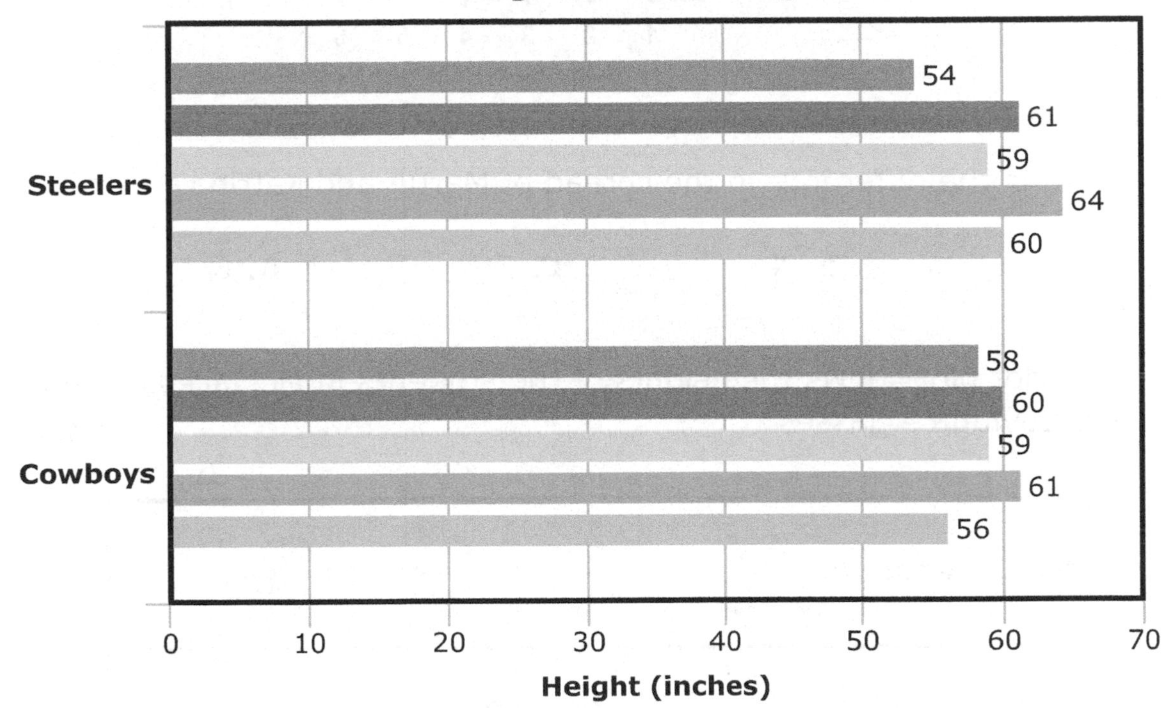

A. equivalent to

B. 1 inch less

C. 2 inches less

D. 2 inches greater

(7.SP.B.3)

6. Martin and Katrina record the number of siblings each of their friends have on these dot plots.

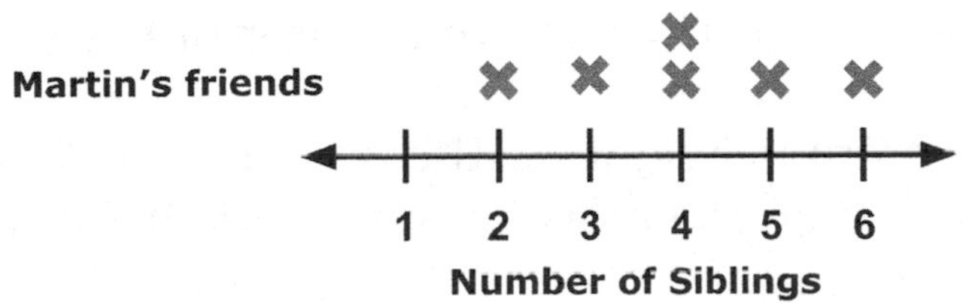

...question 6. continued next page

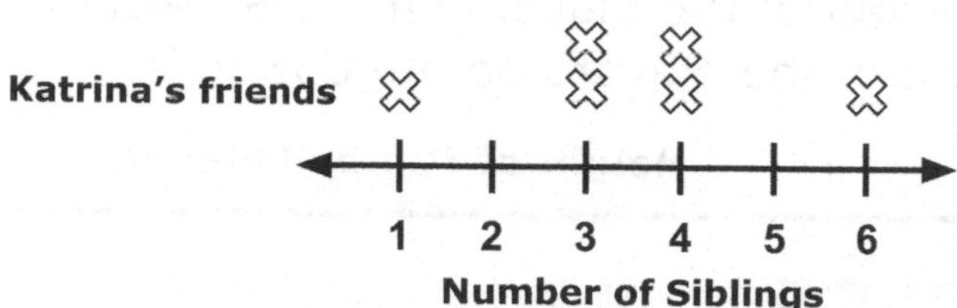

What is the difference in the spread of Martin and Katrina's data?

A. 1 **B.** 4 **C.** 5 **D.** 6

7.SP.B.3

7. This dot plot shows the heights of the students in Mr. Jackson's and Mr. Covinga's classes.

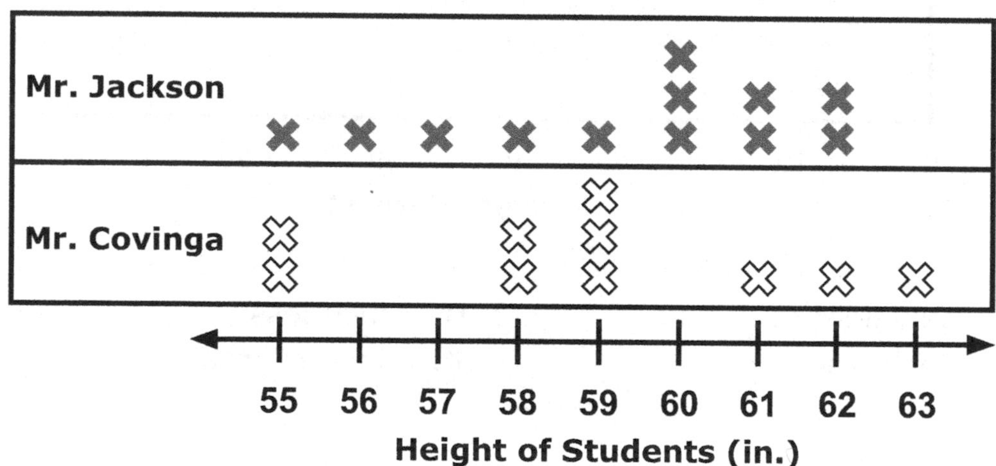

Which statement best describes the center of the data?

A. The most common height for the students in Mr. Jackson's class is 1 inch less than the most common height for the students in Mr. Covinga's class.

B. The data is centered around 58 inches.

...question 7. continued next page

C. The most common height for the students in Mr. Covinga's class is 1 inch less than the most common height for the students in Mr. Jackson's class.

D. The data is centered around 55 inches.

(7.SP.B.3)

8. This dot plot shows the temperatures in two cities over a period of 7-day.

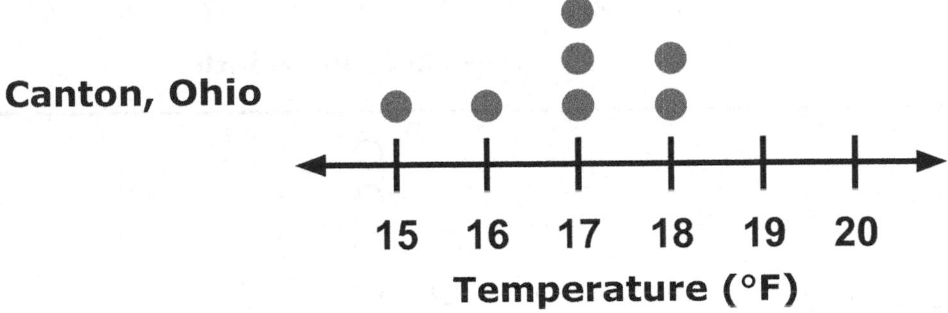

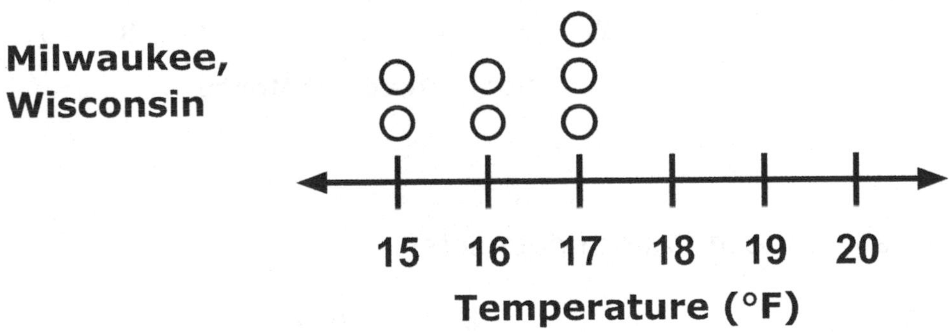

Overall, the median temperature in Canton is __________ degree(s) ______________ than the temperatures in Milwaukee.

(7.SP.B.3)

COMPARE AND INFER TWO POPULATIONS

9. This dot plot shows the number books read by Ms. Wilson and Ms. Smith's classes

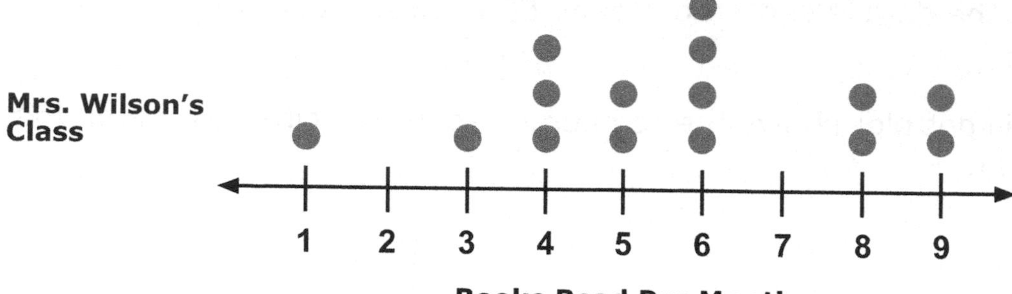

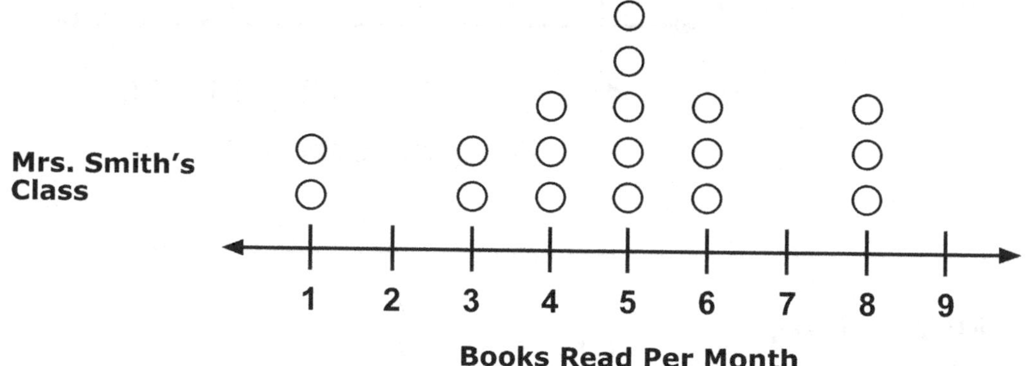

What is the mean of both data sets?

Mrs. Wilson: ______________ Mrs. Smith: ______________

(7.SP.B.3)

10. These dot plots show the times of 8 competitors in two 100-meter dash races.

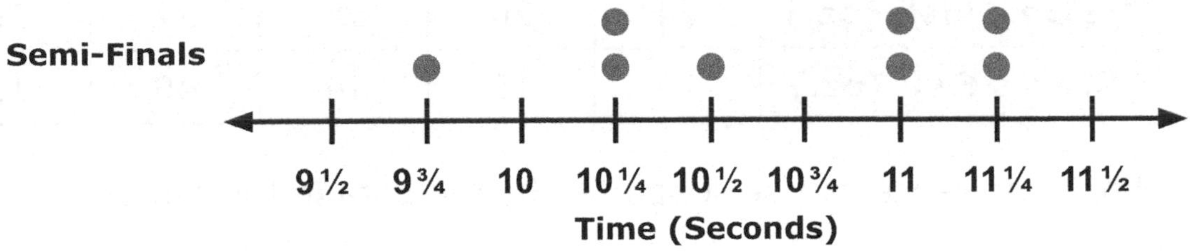

Finals

9½ 9¾ 10 10¼ 10½ 10¾ 11 11¼ 11½

Time (Seconds)

Compare the centers of these dot plots.

____

____

____

____

____

(7.SP.B.3)

11. Justin and Micah are fishing. The weights of 5 fish caught by each person are shown in this table.

Justin's Fish (oz.)	24	20	18	27	30
Micah's Fish (oz.)	19	15	14	40	13

Which inference can be supported by the data in the table?

A. Most of Micah's fish weigh more than 30 ounces.
B. The fish caught by Justin and Micah weigh no more than 35 ounces.
C. Most of Justin's fish weigh more than 20 ounces.
D. The weight of the smallest fish is 14 ounces.

7.SP.B.4

12. Lelita and Yaminah are performing in a singing contest. This table shows the lengths of 4 songs they are preparing.

Lelita's Songs (minutes)	3.75	4	5.25	4.6
Yaminah's Songs (minutes)	3.8	4.2	4	4.5

Which inference can be supported by the data in the table?

A. Neither Lelita or Yaminah will sing a song less than 3.5 minutes long.
B. Yaminah is more likely to sing a 5-minute song.
C. Lelita is more likely to sing a 6-minute song.
D. Both Lelita and Yaminah will sing a song more than 5 minutes long.

7.SP.B.4

13. This table shows the average daily hours of sleep of 10 students in Zane's class and 10 students in Bryson's class.

Zane's Class	9	8	7	6	6	?	9	10	10	8
Bryson's Class	8	8	9	9	9	7	7	6	7	10

The range of Zane's data is greater than the range of Bryson's data. Which value is missing from Zane's data?

A. 10 **B.** 8 **C.** 5 **D.** 6

7.SP.B.4

14. This table shows the average daily hours of sleep of 11 students in Gabriel's class and 11 students in Mario's class.

Gabriel's Class	6	7	8	8	10	11	7	7	9	8	10
Mario's Class	10	11	9	8	8	7	5	6	6	6	9

Which inference can be supported by this data?

A. On average, the students in Gabriel's class sleep 2 more hours than the students in Mario's class.

B. On average, the students in Mario's class sleep less than the students in Gabriel's class.

C. On average, the students in Gabriel's class sleep less than the students in Mario's class.

D. On average, the students in Mario's class sleep 2 more hours than the students in Gabriel's class.

7.SP.B.4

Ace Academic Publishing
ACHIEVING EXCELLENCE TOGETHER

15. Alan and Aki are baking cookies. The values in this table list the amount of time it takes for each batch of cookies to bake.

	Alan's Cookies (minutes)	Aki's Cookies (minutes)
1st	25	16
2nd	25	23
3rd	22	19
4th	30	17
5th	?	?

The mean amount of time it takes for Alan's cookies to bake is 26 minutes, and the mean amount of time it takes for Aki's cookies to bake is 23 minutes.

Which statement can be made about the fifth batch of cookies?

A. Aki's cookies will finish baking 5 minutes after Alan's cookies.

B. Alan's cookies will finish baking 5 minutes after Aki's cookies.

C. Aki's cookies will finish baking 10 minutes after Alan's cookies.

D. Alan's cookies will finish baking 12 minutes before Aki's cookies.

7.SP.B.4

16. Asha and Hattie are baking cookies. The values in this table list the amount of time it takes for each batch of cookies to bake.

	Asha's Cookies (minutes)	Hattie's Cookies (minutes)
1st	?	?
2nd	18	26
3rd	20	29
4th	19	28
5th	21	26

7.SP.B.4

The median amount of time it takes Asha's cookies to bake is 20 minutes.

The median amount of time it takes Hattie's cookies to bake is 27 minutes.

Which inference can be made about each person's first batch of cookies?

A. The difference between Asha's and Hattie's cooking times is 7 minutes.

B. The difference between Asha's and Hattie's cooking times is 10 minutes, but less than 15 minutes.

C. The difference between Asha's and Hattie's cooking times is 15 minutes, but less than 20 minutes.

D. The difference between Asha's and Hattie's cooking times is 20 minutes.

7.SP.B.4

COMPARE AND INFER TWO POPULATIONS

17. Chan Ming and Zoe survey a random sample of 13 students at each of their schools to find out how many students ride the bus.

- Seven out of 13 students at Chan Ming's school ride the bus.
- Four out of 13 students at Zoe's school ride the bus.
- There are 2,050 students at Chan Ming's school.
- Which number is an appropriate prediction of the number of students in the school who ride the bus?

A. 1.100 **B.** 500 **C.** 2.000 **D.** 100

(7.SP.B.4)

18. Cassandra and Nikki plan to determine the average length of the words in their Science textbook. They took a random sample of 8 words from two chapters.

Number of Letters (Chapter 1)	?	9	6	7	12	11	10	5
Number of Letters (Chapter 2)	?	7	6	7	12	2	6	7

The mean word length for Chapter 1 is 8 letters, and the mean word length for Chapter 2 is 7 letters.

The missing value for Chapter 1 is ________ letters longer than the missing value for Chapter 2.

(7.SP.B.4)

19. Holden and Ethan plan to determine the average length of the words in their Mathematics textbook. They took a random sample of 10 words from two chapters.

Chapter 1	8	7	6	10	4	3	9	?	2	1
Chapter 2	10	9	5	7	6	4	8	9	10	10

The range of the word lengths for Chapter 1 is 4 letters greater than the range of word lengths for Chapter 2.

What is the missing number from this data set? ____________

7.SP.B.4

20. This bar graph shows the height of a random sample of football players from 2 teams.

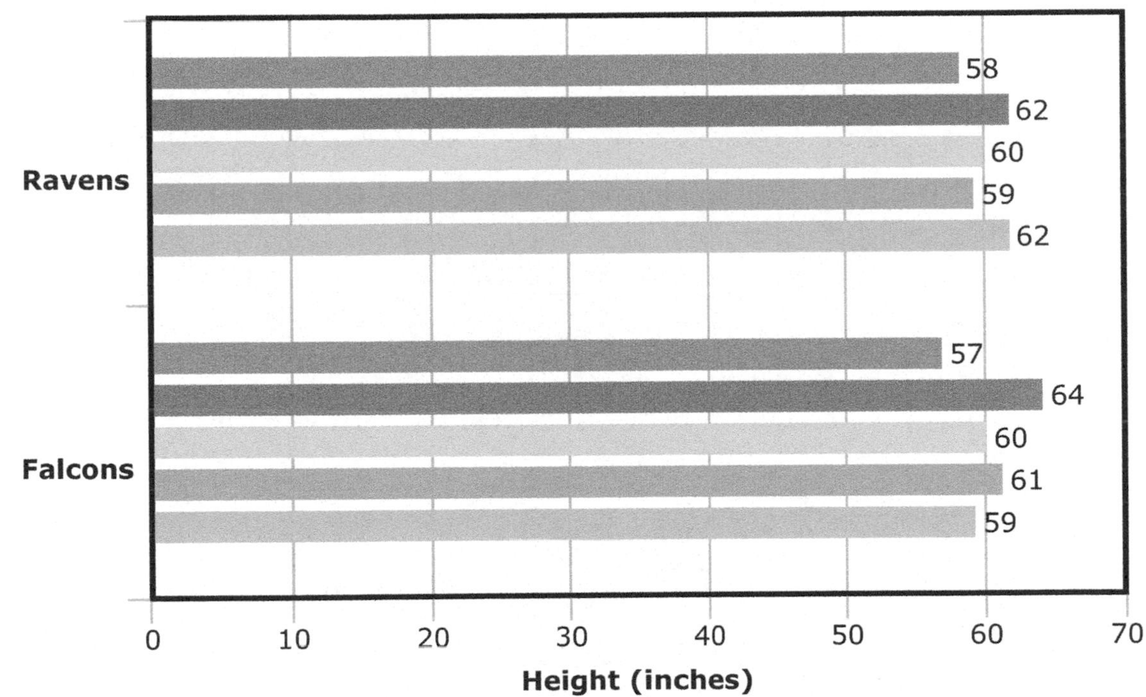

...question 20. continued next page

What can you infer about the height of the players?

____

____

____

7.SP.B.4

Ace Academic Publishing
ACHIEVING EXCELLENCE TOGETHER

www.aceacademicprep.com

1. Joseph has a bag with 12 marbles. The marbles are blue, white, green and red. What is the probability of drawing a black marble from Joseph's bag?

A. unlikely **B.** impossible
C. neither unlikely or likely **D.** certain

7.SP.C.5

2. Larson has a bag with 15 marbles. There are 2 blue, 1 white, 6 black and 6 yellow marbles inside the bag. What is the probability of drawing a white marble from Larson's bag?

A. unlikely **B.** impossible
C. neither unlikely or likely **D.** certain

7.SP.C.5

3. Kumal has a bag with 14 marbles. There are 10 red, 1 green, 2 black and 2 purple marbles inside the bag. What is the probability of drawing a red marble from Kumal's bag?

A. unlikely **B.** impossible
C. neither unlikely or likely **D.** certain

7.SP.C.5

4. Drea rolls a six-sided number cube. What is the probability the number cube will land on a number greater than 1?

____

7.SP.C.5

5. Ivy rolls a six-sided number cube. The numbers on the cube are the first six prime numbers between 1 and 15. What is the probability she will land on a number less than 7?

____

7.SP.C.5

STATISTICS AND PROBABILITY

6. James rolls a six-sided number cube 450 times. The numbers on the cube are 1 through 6.

   Which value is a prediction of the number times the cube will land on a 3?

   A. 300 **B.** 75 **C.** 375 **D.** 200

   7.SP.C.6

7. Lily rolls a six-sided number cube 200 time. The numbers on the cube are 1 through 6.

   Which value is a prediction of the number times the cube will land on 2 or 4?

   A. 200 **B.** 100 **C.** 90 **D.** 67

   7.SP.C.6

8. Irving surveys 24 students to determine their favorite colors. Of the students he surveyed, 8 said their favorite color was red.

   What is the experimental probability that the next student Irving talks to will say their favorite color is red?

   A. $\frac{1}{3}$ **B.** $\frac{1}{6}$ **C.** $\frac{1}{4}$ **D.** $\frac{1}{10}$

   7.SP.C.6

9. William is randomly drawing straws from a bag. He draws 2 straws that are 1-inch long, 7 straws that are 2-inches long, and 4 straws that are 3-inches long.

   There are 60 straws in the bag. what is a prediction of the number of straws are 2-inches long.

   ____

   7.SP.C.6

10. Martin asks his friends which movie they like best. He surveys 16 friends, and 10 like *Shrek*.

What is the experimental probability that the next friend Martin surveys will like *Shrek*?

____

7.SP.C.6

11. Desiree created these spinners.

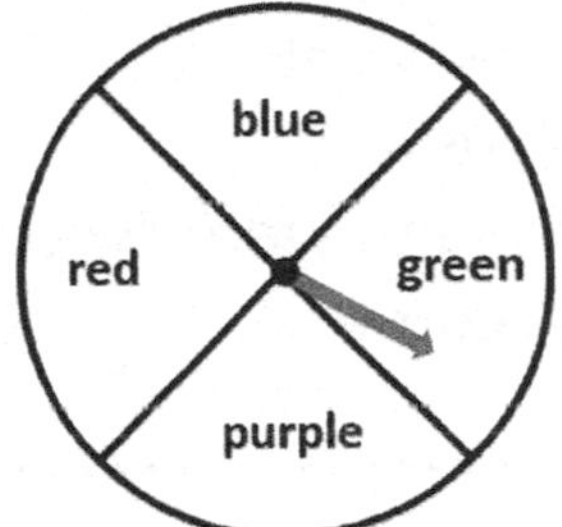

She spins both spinners at the same time. After 10 spins, these are her results:

(1, red), (3, green), (3, purple), (1, blue), (2, red)
(2, green), (1, blue), (3, purple), (1, red), (1, green)

Which statement could explain the discrepancy between the theoretical probability and Desiree's actual results?

A. The largest region on the numbered spinner contains a "3".

B. The "1" spaces on the numbered spinner are actually wider than the figure shows.

C. Each region on the spinner with colors is equal.

D. The probability of landing on a color is greater than landing on a number.

7.SP.C.7

12. Doug rolls standard dice 10 times. He observes $\frac{3}{10}$ of his rolls resulted in a three. Doug combines his results with the other students in his class and discovers $\frac{3}{8}$ of the rolls for the entire class resulted in a three.

How do the results of Doug's class compare to the expected fraction of possible outcomes for rolling a three?

A. The class results were greater than the expected fraction of possible outcomes.

B. The class results were less than the expected fraction of possible outcomes.

C. The class results and the expected fraction of possible outcomes were the same.

D. The class results were twice as large as the expected fraction of possible outcomes.

(7.SP.C.7)

13. Mark rolls two standard die 10 times. He observes $\frac{5}{10}$ of his rolls resulted in at least one five. Mark combines his results with the other students in his class and discovers $\frac{11}{40}$ of the rolls for the entire class resulted in at least one five.

How do the results of Mark's class compare to the fraction of possible outcomes for rolling at least one five?

A. The class results were greater than the expected fraction of possible outcomes.

B. The class results were less than the expected fraction of possible outcomes.

C. The class results and the expected fraction of possible outcomes were the same.

D. The class results were twice as large as the expected fraction of possible outcomes.

(7.SP.C.7)

14. Holton rolls a pair of die 15 times. This is a list of his outcomes.

(1,3), (4,4), (3,6), (6,6), (1,2),

(3,4), (5,2), (2,1), (4,5), (6,3),

(5,2), (3,3), (4,5), (5,5), (1,1)

Holton decides to roll the pair of die 50 more times. Based on his results, what is the probability the die will have a sum of 7 from those 50 rolls?

____

(7.SP.C.7)

15. Niko is determining the probability of randomly selecting a letter from the word "mathematics". He records his first 20 selections in this table.

Selection	1	2	3	4	5	6	7	8	9	10	11	12	13	14	15	16	17	18	19	20
Outcome	m	a	s	t	h	i	c	i	s	e	h	m	h	e	i	m	m	s	c	a

Using the data from his experiment, what is Niko's estimate for the probability of selecting the letter "h"?

____

(7.SP.C.7)

16. There are 12 students auditioning for 3 parts in the school play. How many combinations of students are possible?

A. 36 **B.** 220 **C.** 1.320 **D.** 1.728

(7.SP.C.8)

PROBABILITY MODELS

17. Michael rolls two number cubes and flips a coin. One number cube is labeled with the numbers 0-5, and the second number cube is labeled with the numbers 1-6. He records each flip of the coin as heads up, H, or tails up, T.

How many possible outcomes will Michael have by rolling two number cubes and flipping a coin?

A. 72 **B.** 36 **C.** 18 **D.** 14

7.SP.C.8

18. Mrs. Johnson wants to organize 5-person teams for an upcoming project. There are 19 students in Mrs. Johnson's class. Which expression represents the number of possible combinations?

A. ${}_{5}C_{19}$ **B.** ${}_{14}C_{5}$ **C.** ${}_{5}C_{14}$ **D.** ${}_{19}C_{5}$

7.SP.C.8

19. Mr. Johnson prepares sandwiches for his children using these ingredients.

Bread	Meat	Cheese	Vegetable
Wheat White Rye	Ham Salami Turkey	Swiss American Pepper Jack	Pickles Tomatoes Lettuce Onion

How many different combinations of sandwiches can Mr. Johnson prepare?

____

7.SP.C.8

20. A restaurant creates pizza using these ingredients.

Crust	Meat	Sauce	Vegetable
Regular Thin Pan-Style	Sausage Pepperoni Hamburger Bacon	Tomato Ranch BBQ	Onion Mushroom Tomato Bell Pepper Olive

How many different combinations of pizzas can this restaurant prepare?

____

(7.SP.C.8)

1. Marquan is preparing to fly from Honolulu to Seattle. There are 150 passengers on the flight. Marquan determines 16% of the passengers are children.

   Which response describes a random sample Marquan could have used to make this prediction?

   A. Marquan counted the number of children in 10 rows on the plane.
   B. Marquan asked the person sitting next to him to predict how many passengers are children.
   C. Marquan asked the 4 flight attendants how many of the passengers are children.
   D. Marquan counts the number of seats on the plane.

(7.SP.A.1)

2. Parth places 30 marbles inside a bag. The marbles are blue, black, and red. He reaches inside the bag, draws one red and one blue marble, then determines the bag is 50% red marbles and 50% blue marbles.

   Is Parth's conclusion representative of the type of marbles in the bag?

   ____

   ____

   ____

   ____

   ____

(7.SP.A.1)

3. Beatrice designs 3 surveys to determine the favorite colors of the students in her school. The results of her surveys are in this table.

Survey	Number of People Surveyed	Favorite Colors			
		Red	Blue	Green	Yellow
A	25	12	9	4	4
B	22	9	7	4	2
C	30	13	10	4	3

There are 360 students in Beatrice's school. Based on this data, which color will approximately $\frac{1}{3}$ of the students in Beatrice's school select as their favorite?

____

(7.SP.A.2)

4. The data in this bar graph shows the different sports played by the students in Jada's class.

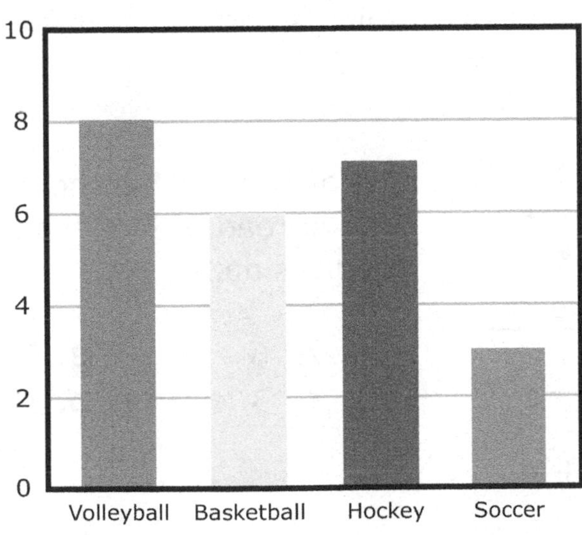

There are 200 students in Jada's school. Using this data to make inferences about the entire school, how many students play basketball?

A. 140

B. 100

C. 50

D. 10

(7.SP.A.2)

CHAPTER REVIEW

5. This dot plot shows the temperatures in two cities over a 7-day period.

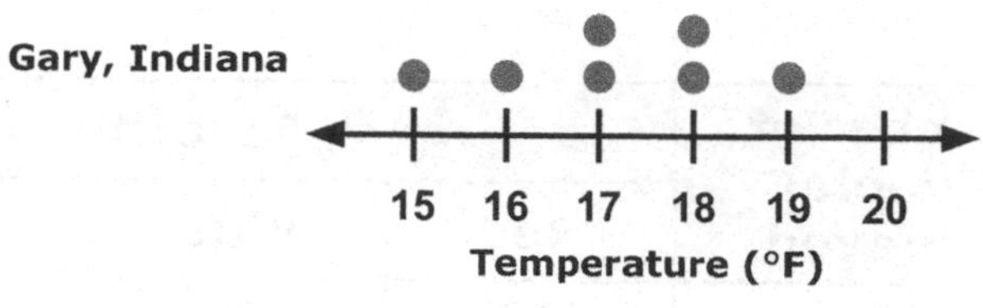

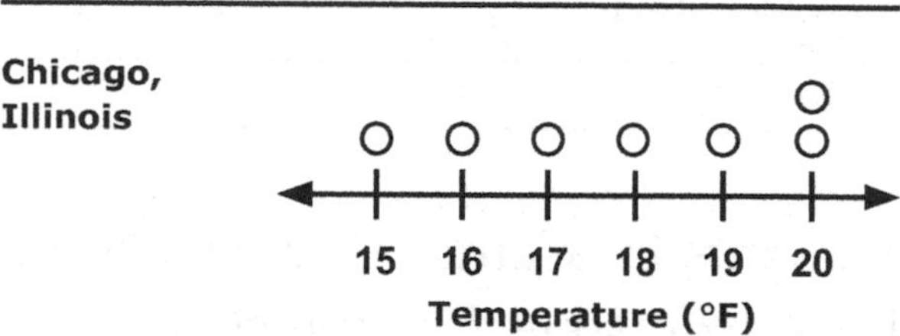

The data within the dot plot for Gary, Indiana is clustered around the value

____

(7.SP.B.3)

6. Isabel and Pedro record the number of siblings each of their friends have on these dot plots.

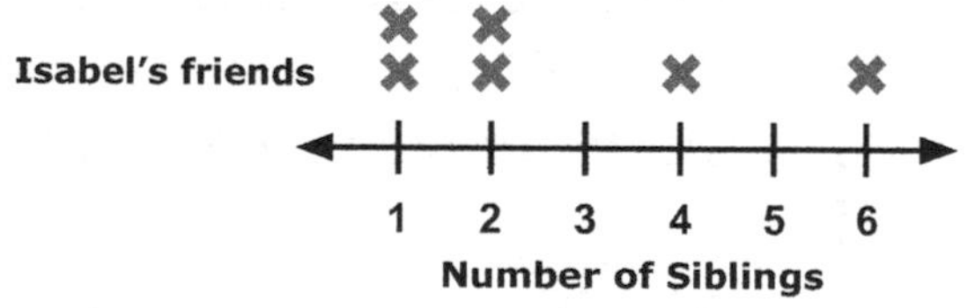

Pedro's friends

1 2 3 4 5 6

Number of Siblings

What is the difference in the spread of Isabel and Pedro's data?

A. 6 **B.** 5
C. 3 **D.** 1

(7.SP.B.3)

7. Ava asks two groups of seventh grade students how many pets they own. This table show a random sample of the students who participated in Ava's survey.

Group A	?	3	2	3	2	3
Group B	?	0	0	2	1	1

The range of the data in Group A is 2 pets, and the range of the data in Group B is 4 pets. Which inference can be supported by the data in the table?

A. The greatest number of pets owned by students in Group B is 4.

B. The greatest number of pets owned by students in Group A is 2.

C. The greatest number of pets owned by students in Group B is 4.

D. The greatest number of pets owned by students in Group A is 6.

(7.SP.B.4)

8. Jarrah is drawing marbles out of a bag. She determines the chances of selecting a red marble out of the bag is unlikely. Which combination could describe the colors of the marbles in her bag?

A. 1 red, 1 blue, 1 green
B. 9 red, 1 blue, 1 green
C. 9 green, 2 red, 7 blue
D. 4 green, 5 blue, 1 black

(7.SP.B.4)

9. Everett is drawing marbles out of a bag. He determines the chances of selecting a black marble out of the bag is neither unlikely or likely. Which combination could describe the marbles in his bag?

A. 9 blue, 1 black
B. 8 green, 2 blue
C. 9 black, 1 blue
D. 5 black, 5 blue

(7.SP.C.5)

CHAPTER REVIEW

10. Lucy is drawing marbles out of a bag. She determines the chances of selecting a white marble out of the bag is impossible. Which response could describe the marbles in her bag?

A. 5 green, 1 yellow, 1 white
B. 4 black, 2 white, 8 green
C. 3 blue, 2 black, 4 green
D. 7 black, 7 white, 7 red

(7.SP.C.5)

11. Dara and David plan to determine the average length of the words in their Language Arts textbook. They took a random sample of 9 words from two chapters.

Number of Letters (Chapter 1)	5	?	7	9	10	11	2	2	5
Number of Letters (Chapter 2)	8	?	6	9	5	10	11	12	7

The mean word length for Chapter 1 is 7 letters, and the mean word length for Chapter 2 is 8 letters.

The missing value for Chapter 1 is ____________ letters longer than the missing value for Chapter 2.

(7.SP.C.5)

12. Kyle has a box of 150 pencils. Each time he draws a pencil from the box, he replaces it. After 60 draws, Kyle selects 37 yellow pencils, and 23 black pencils.

Which value is an accurate prediction of the number of black pencils inside Kyle's box?

A. 93 **B.** 125 **C.** 57 **D.** 43

(7.SP.C.6)

13. Taren has a box of 180 pencils. Each time he draws a pencil from the box, he replaces it. After 20 draws, Taren selects 8 white pencils, 2 blue pencils, and 10 green pencils.

Which value is an accurate prediction of the number of blue pencils inside Taren's box?

A. 18 **B.** 72 **C.** 90 **D.** 108

7.SP.C.6

14. Olivia has a box of 225 pencils. Each time she draws a pencil from the box, she replaces it. After 30 draws, Olivia selects 15 red pencils, 9 black pencils, and 8 green pencils.

What is the experimental probability Olivia will select a red pencil on her next draw?

A. $\frac{30}{225}$ **B.** $\frac{9}{30}$ **C.** $\frac{13}{30}$ **D.** $\frac{1}{15}$

7.SP.C.6

15. A number cube contains the numbers 1 through 6. Which probability model represents the chance of rolling an odd number on this number cube?

A. $P(odd) = \frac{\text{number of possibilities for rolling a 1 or 3}}{\text{total number of faces on the number cube}}$

B. $P(odd) = \frac{\text{number of possibilities for rolling a 1 or 2}}{\text{total number of faces on the number cube}}$

C. $P(odd) = \frac{\text{number of possibilities for rolling an odd number}}{\text{total number of faces on the number cube}}$

D. $P(odd) = \frac{\text{total number of faces on the number cube}}{\text{number of possibilities for rolling an odd number}}$

7.SP.C.7

CHAPTER REVIEW

CHAPTER REVIEW

16. A number cube contains the numbers 1 through 6. Which probability model represents the chance of rolling a multiple of 2 on this number cube?

A. $P(multiple) = \dfrac{\text{number of possibilities for rolling an even number}}{\text{total number of faces on the number cube}}$

B. $P(multiple) = \dfrac{\text{number of possibilities for rolling a 2 or 4}}{\text{total number of faces on the number cube}}$

C. $P(multiple) = \dfrac{\text{number of possibilities for rolling a 2}}{\text{total number of faces on the number cube}}$

D. $P(multiple) = \dfrac{\text{total number of faces on the number cube}}{\text{number of possibilities for rolling an even number}}$

(7.SP.C.7)

17. A number cube contains the numbers 1 through 6. Which probability model represents the chance of rolling a number less than 4 on this number cube?

A. $P(less\ than\ 4) = \dfrac{\text{number of possibilities for rolling an even number}}{\text{total number of faces on the number cube}}$

B. $P(less\ than\ 4) = \dfrac{\text{number of possibilities for rolling a 1,2 or 3}}{\text{total number of faces on the number cube}}$

C. $P(less\ than\ 4) = \dfrac{\text{number of possibilities for rolling a 1,2,3,or 4}}{\text{total number of faces on the number cube}}$

D. $P(less\ than\ 4) = \dfrac{\text{total number of faces on the number cube}}{\text{number of possibilities for rolling a 1,2,3,or 4}}$

(7.SP.C.7)

18. Nathan rolls two number cubes labeled with the numbers 1-6. Rolling each number cube is an independent event. What is the probability Nathan will roll an even number on the first cube and a five on the second cube?

A. $\frac{1}{4}$ **B.** $\frac{1}{12}$ **C.** $\frac{2}{3}$ **D.** $\frac{1}{6}$

(7.SP.C.8)

19. Lila's mother is catering a birthday party. She provides fish or chicken as the main entrée and offers the guests 3 different side vegetables. This table shows the meal selections of the first 45 people who attend the party.

	Salad	Rice	Squash
Fish	7	9	5
Chicken	7	8	9

Based on these results, what is the experimental probability that the next person will order a fish dinner with squash?

A. $\frac{5}{28}$ **B.** $\frac{14}{45}$ **C.** $\frac{1}{5}$ **D.** $\frac{14}{31}$

(7.SP.C.8)

20. Roberta flips 3 coins. She records the possibilities of flipping each coin heads up, H, and tails up, T, in a list. Each coin flip is an independent event. Which response shows all the combinations in the sample set?

A. HHH, TTT, HTH

B. HHH, TTT, TTH, HHT

C. HHH, HHT, HTH, HTT, THH, THT, TTH, TTT

D. HHH, HHT, HTH, HTT, TTT

(7.SP.C.8)

STATISTICS AND PROBABILITY

EXTRA PRACTICE

1. Paola's family is opening a restaurant. On the first day, they have over 500 customers. On the second day, they have over 700 customers. Paola creates a satisfaction survey and emails it to 100 of the customers who visited to the restaurant on the first day, and 140 of the customer who visited the restaurant on the second day.

Will Paola's data be biased or representative of all the customers who came to the restaurant in the first two days?

____

(7.SP.A.1)

2. Lee has 12 coins in a jar. He randomly draws 5 dimes, 4 pennies, and 1 nickel from the jar without replacing any coins. What does his selection tell you about the number of dimes, pennies and nickels in the jar?

____

____

____

(7.SP.A.1)

3. This table shows the number of male and female monkey at 5 different city zoos.

Male Monkeys	10	8	9	11	7
Female Monkeys	12	9	11	23	8

Using this data, in a larger zoo population of 55 monkeys approximately how many are male?

____

(7.SP.A.2)

4. Dawn recognizes there are 4 prime numbers between 1 and 10. She estimates there will be 40 prime numbers between 1 and 100.

Do you agree with Dawn? Explain your reasoning.

____

____

____

(7.SP.A.2)

5. These box plots compare the test scores of students in two classes.

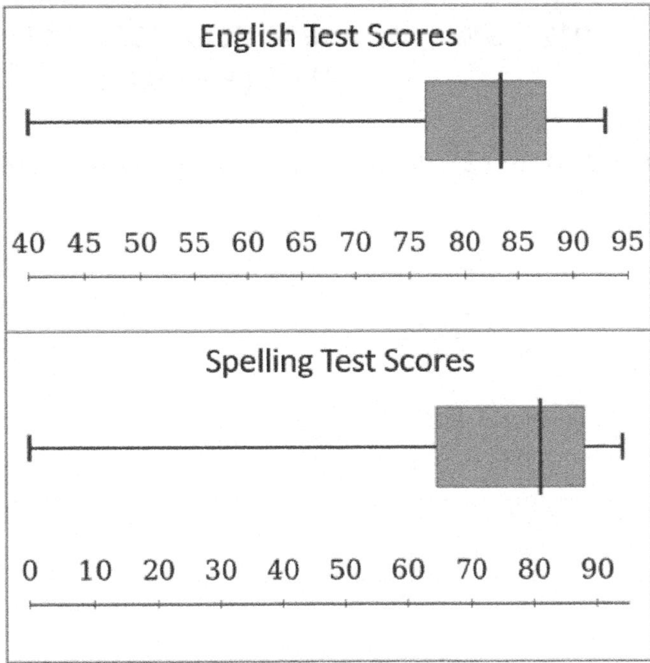

Which box plot has a greater range?

____

(7.SP.B.3)

EXTRA PRACTICE

6. These dot plots show the official completion times of 8 competitors participating in two 100-meter dash races.

Semi-Finals

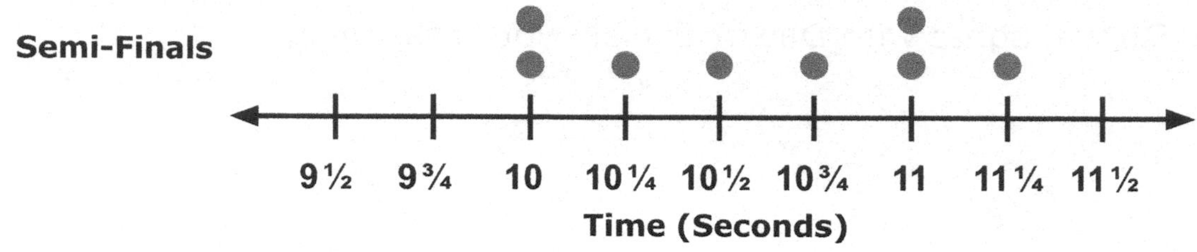

Finals

9½ 9¾ 10 10¼ 10½ 10¾ 11 11¼ 11½

Time (Seconds)

How would you compare the shape of these dot plots?

____

____

____

____

____

____

____

____

(7.SP.B.3)

EXTRA PRACTICE

7. Mrs. Jeffries asked a random sample of students in two classes what size shoe they wear. The results are shown on these dot plots.

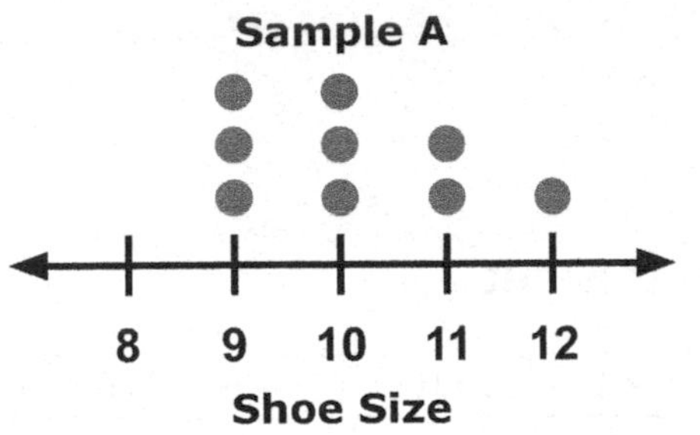

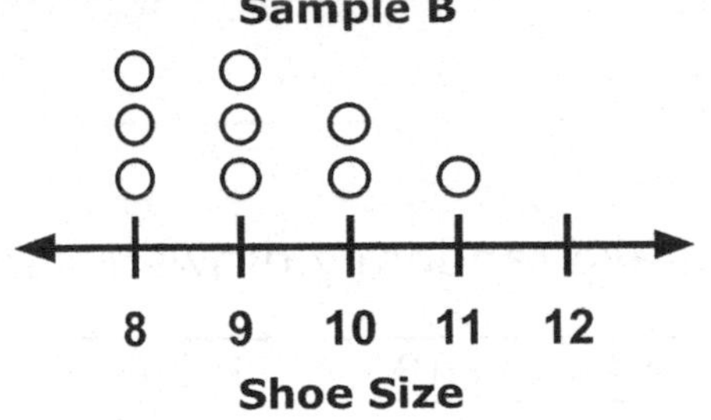

What can you infer about the students' shoe size from this data?

____

____

(7.SP.B.4)

8. Mr. Janus asked a random sample of students in two classes what size shoe they wear. The results are shown on this dot plot.

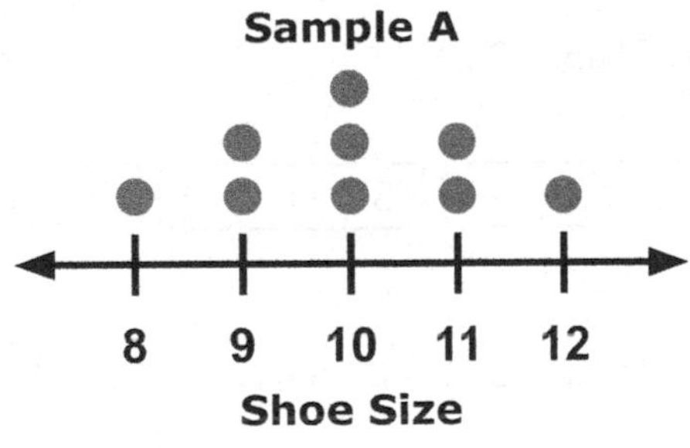

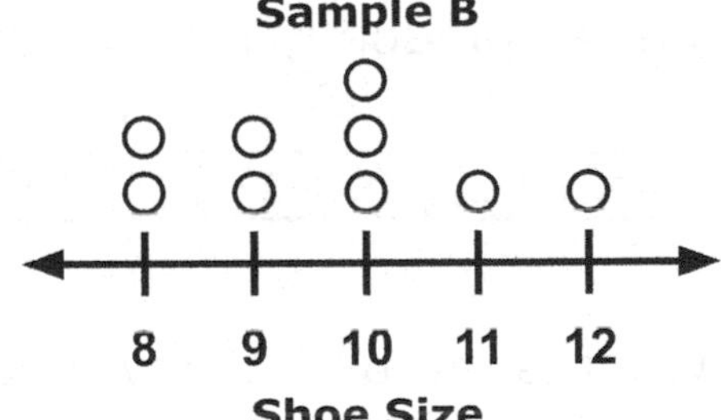

What can you infer about the students' shoe size from this data?

____

____

(7.SP.B.4)

EXTRA PRACTICE

9. Thomas rolls a six-sided number cube. The numbers on the cube are the first six prime numbers between 1 and 15. What is the probability she will land on a 1?

____

7.SP.C.5

10. Natalia randomly draws a card from this set.

$(2 \times 4 + 1)$	$(8 \div 4 - 1)$	$(9 + 9 + 2)$	$(7 \times 2 - 3)$	$(5 + 5 + 5)$	$(6 - 1 + 7)$

What is the probability of Natalia selecting a card with an expression that is equal to an even number? Explain your reasoning.

____

____

____

7.SP.C.5

11. Xavier randomly draws a card from this set.

$(3 \times 4 + 2)$	$(4 \div 4 + 1)$	$(9 + 7 + 2)$	$(5 \times 2 - 2)$	$(5 + 4 + 5)$	$(8 - 1 + 7)$

What is the probability that Xavier draws a card with an expression that is equal to an odd number?

____

____

____

7.SP.C.5

12. Each hour, 15 buses arrive in downtown Dallas, Texas. Of these buses, 3 are from Houston, Texas.

What is the experimental probability the next bus will be from Houston?

______

7.SP.C.6

13. At a basketball game, 14 out of the first 20 attendees is male. Howard determines $\frac{7}{10}$ of the attendees will be male, and $\frac{3}{10}$ will be female. Do you agree with Howard? Explain your reasoning.

______

______

______

7.SP.C.6

14. A spinner has 4 equal sections. Each section is identified by a color: red, blue, yellow, and green.

After 18 spins, Lucy lands on blue 8 times. What is the experimental probability of landing on blue? Why?

______

______

______

______

7.SP.C.6

EXTRA PRACTICE

15. Lynn develops this chart by recording the outcomes of rolling two number cubes and calculating their products.

		Number Cube #1					
		1	2	3	4	5	6
Number Cube #2	1	1	2	3	4	5	6
	2	2	4	6	8	10	12
	3	3	6	9	12	15	18
	4	4	8	12	16	20	24
	5	5	10	15	20	25	30
	6	6	12	18	24	30	36

What is the probability of rolling two numbers with a product greater than 15?

____

7.SP.C.7

16. Miles and his friends are planning to use 2 number cubes for a game they created.

The first number cube is labeled with the first six multiples of 2. The second number cube is labeled with the first six multiples of 3. Is the probability of rolling each unique number on the number cubes the same? Explain.

____

____

____

7.SP.C.7

17. Fredo and his friends are planning to use 2 number cubes for a game they created.

The first number cube is labeled with the first six prime numbers. The second number cube is labeled with the first six even numbers after 0. Is the probability of rolling each unique number on the number cubes the same? Explain.

____

____

____

(7.SP.C.7)

18. Mr. and Mrs. Langley are creating a menu of possible family meals. One meal must contain an entrée, a vegetable, a bread, and a dessert. They ask their children to choose from these options.

Entrée	Vegetable	Bread	Dessert
Beef Stew	Potatoes	Croissants	Apple Pie
Fried Chicken	Green Beans	Dinner Rolls	Peach Cobbler
Meatloaf	Carrots		Ice Cream
BBQ Beef	Corn		

How many meals combinations are possible?

____

____

____

(7.SP.C.8)

Ace Academic Publishing
ACHIEVING EXCELLENCE TOGETHER

EXTRA PRACTICE

19. The letters that form the word TENNESSEE are placed in a bowl. What is the probability of choosing a consonant letter, replacing it and then drawing a "S"?

____

____

____

7.SP.C.8

20. Rudy has a jar of marbles with the following colors: 3 orange, 8 green, and 5 black. What is the probability of selecting a marble from the jar that is not green, and then selecting one that is orange without replacing the first marble?

____

____

____

7.SP.C.8

COMPREHENSIVE ASSESSMENTS

Ace Academic Publishing
ACHIEVING EXCELLENCE TOGETHER

www.aceacademicprep.com

ASSESSMENT 1

COMPREHENSIVE ASSESSMENTS

1. Fred wants to find the best deal on apples. He can purchase 5 apples for $2.85 or 7 peaches for $3.50. Which type of fruit cost less?

____

(7.RP.A.1)

2. Laundry Detergent A costs $4.99 for 25 fluid ounces and Laundry Detergent B costs $7.49 for 90 fluid ounces. Which laundry detergent cost has the lowest unit cost?

____

(7.RP.A.1)

3. Jeff earns $12 an hour raking leaves. Write an equation to express his earnings y in terms of how many hours x he works.

____

(7.RP.A.2)

4. Thomas estimates that the weight of his dog is 55 pounds. The actual weight is 68 pounds. What is the percent error Thomas made?

   A. 13%   **B.** 16%   **C.** 19%   **D.** 22%

(7.RP.A.3)

5. Lauren deposited started her bank account with a deposit of $300. After one year, she had $312 in her account. If she did not make any deposits, how much interest did she earn from her bank account?

____

(7.RP.A.3)

ASSESSMENT 1

6. Evaluate $-6+15-(-8)+2$

A. -17 **B.** 19 **C.** 5 **D.** -16

(7.NS.A.1)

7. What is the value of $-378-(-378)$?

A. 0 **B.** -378 **C.** 378 **D.** -756

(7.NS.A.1)

8. If $a=\frac{5}{6}$ and $b=-18$, what is $-a \times b$?

A. -15 **B.** 6 **C.** 15 **D.** -6

(7.NS.A.2)

9. Simplify: $-2-6+9-7$

A. -6 **B.** -22 **C.** -14 **D.** -23

(7.NS.A.2)

10. Caitlyn has \$82 to spend. She wants to purchase of an item that costs \$96. How much money does she need to borrow to make the purchase?

____

(7.NS.A.3)

11. Which expression correctly represents this statement?

The difference between the product of two-thirds and a number x and the product of one-half and the same number

A. $\frac{2}{3}x+\frac{1}{2}x$ **B.** $\frac{2}{6}-x$ **C.** $(\frac{2}{3})-(\frac{1}{2})(x)$ **D.** $\frac{1}{6}x$

(7.EE.A.1)

12. A store is selling items at a discount. This expression represents the original price of the item m with a 24.5% discount.

$$m - 0.245m$$

Which expression also represents this discount?

A. $1.245m$ **B.** $1.755m$ **C.** $1.45m$ **D.** $0.755m$

7.EE.A.2

13. Write an expression, without parentheses, in Column B that is equivalent to the one shown in Column A.

Column A	Column B
$\frac{3}{7}(2x+5)+\frac{3}{7}$	

Describe the process you would use to create the equivalent expression.

____

____

____

7.EE.A.2

14. Tomas uses 12 gallons of water to prepare lemonade for a party. The lemonade recipe states that for every 2 quarts of water, he should add $\frac{1}{2}$ cup of lemon juice and $\frac{2}{3}$ cup of sugar.

How much lemon juice does Tomas need?

A. 3 cups **B.** 24 cups **C.** 6 cups **D.** 12 cups

7.EE.B.3

15. Dana is driving east toward a gas station, passes by the station and continues driving. She uses this number line to represent the distance she is east of the station.

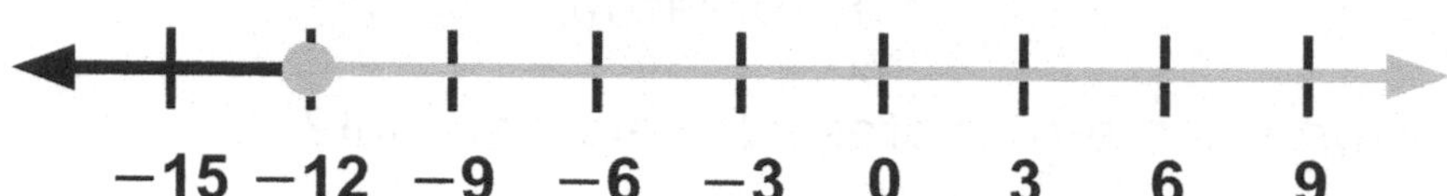

Which inequality represents this number line?

A. $x < -12$ **B.** $x > -12$ **C.** $x \geq -12$ **D.** $x \leq -12$

(7.EE.B.4)

16. Bryshon uses this scale to draw a map of the Nile River.

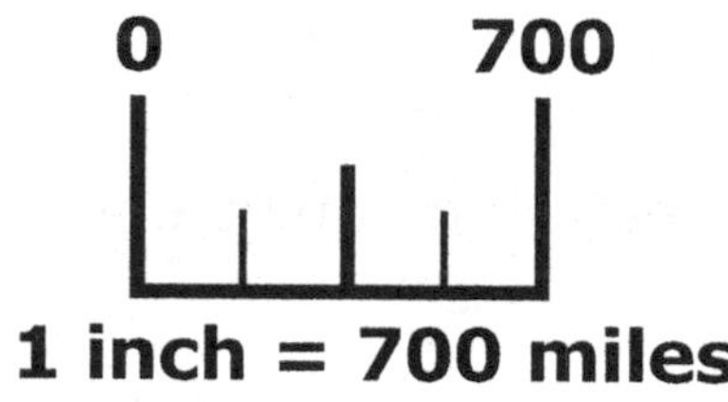

The actual length of the Nile River is 4,258 miles. He estimates the length of the river on his map will be approximately 6 inches.

Do you agree with Bryshon? Explain your reasoning.

____

____

____

____

____

____

(7.G.A.1)

17. This drawing is a scale model of Jason's bedroom.

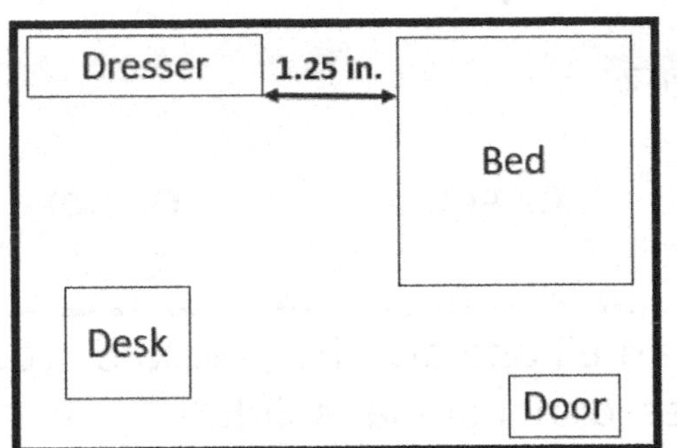

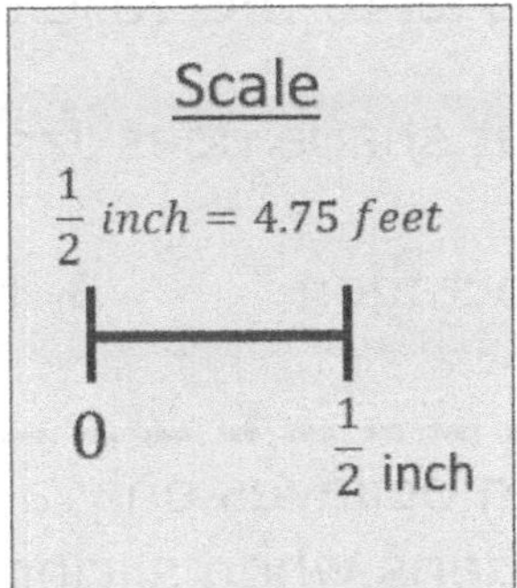

Which expression represents the area of the room, in square feet?

A. $2(6) + 2(4)$
B. $(2 \cdot 12 \cdot 4.75) + (2 \cdot 8 \cdot 4.75)$
C. $4(6)$
D. $(12 \cdot 4.75)(8 \cdot 4.75)$

(7.G.A.1)

18. Jolene is constructing a triangle. The length of two sides are 5 centimeters and 4 centimeters.

Which length could represent the third side of Jolene's triangle?

A. 1 cm **B.** 3 cm **C.** 9 cm **D.** 10 cm

(7.G.A.2)

19. Toshi is constructing a triangle with these conditions:

- The length of one side is 8.5 inches
- The length of one side is 1.5 inches

What are the possible whole number lengths of the triangle's third side?

____

(7.G.A.2)

ASSESSMENT 1

20. Janine takes a cross section of an 8-sided prism. Her cross section is parallel to the base of the prism.

What shape does Janine create?

A. octagon **B.** heptagon **C.** square **D.** hexagon

(7.G.A.3)

21. Leah believes only a circle or an ellipse are the possible cross sections when slicing this three-dimensional solid.

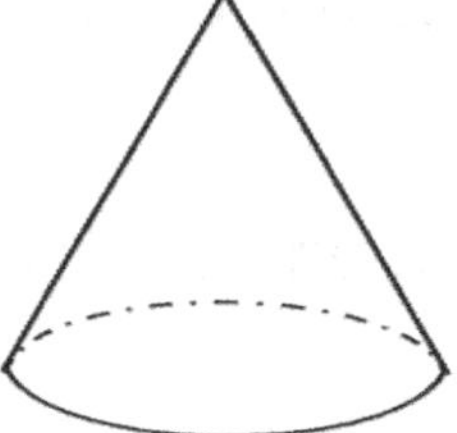

Do you agree with Leah? Why? Or why not?

____

____

____

____

(7.G.A.3)

22. A circular watch has a diameter of 19.5 millimeters. What is the area of the watch?

A. $61.23\,mm^2$ **B.** $121.10\,mm^2$ **C.** $298.50\,mm^2$ **D.** $1{,}193.99\,mm^2$

(7.G.B.4)

23. This figure shows a small circle placed in the center of an large circle.

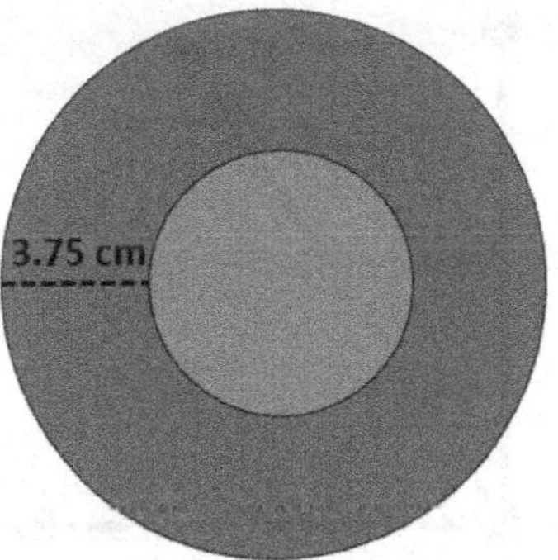

The area of the large circle is 49 π square centimeters. What is the exact area, in square centimeters, of the small circle?

____

7.G.B.4

24. The measure of ∠ RST is 60°. What is the value of x?

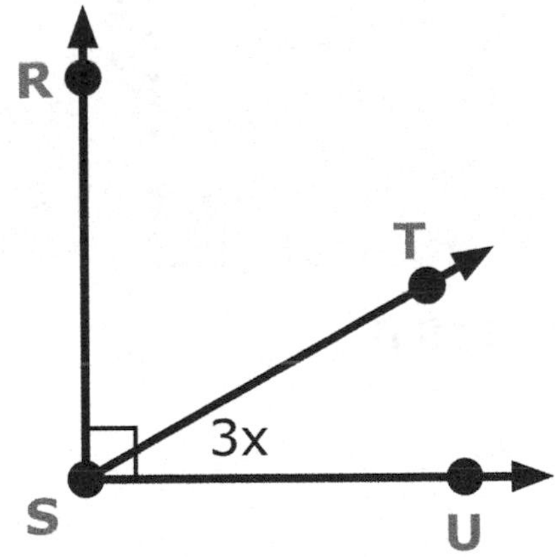

____

7.G.B.5

ASSESSMENT 1

25. What is the measure, in degree, of ∠ DEF?

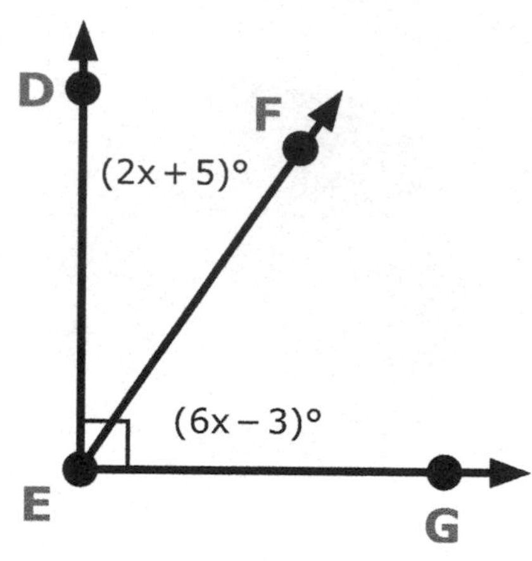

(7.G.B.5)

26. What is the area of this playground?

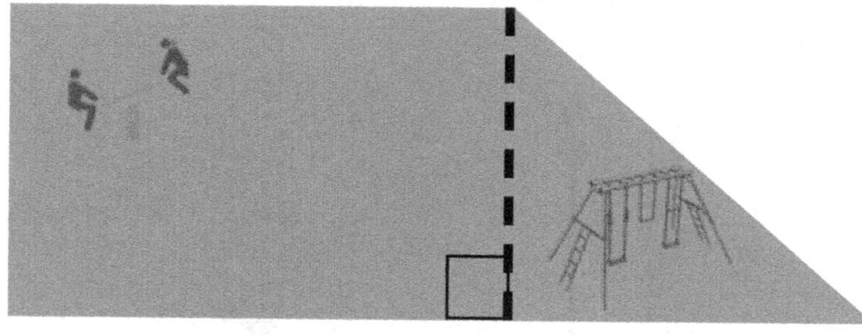

A. 3,888 ft^2 **B.** 7,830 ft^2 **C.** 1,971 ft^2 **D.** 5,859 ft^2

(7.G.B.6)

27. How many cubes with a side length of 2 inches will fit inside this rectangular prism?

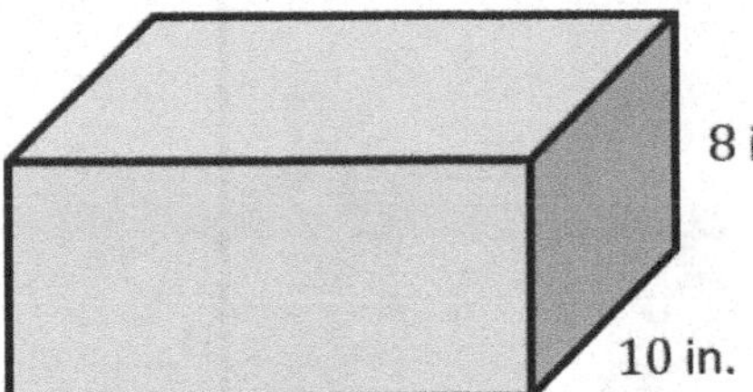

____

____

____

(7.G.B.6)

28. Imani is planning to conduct a survey to determine which animals the people in her town like the most. Which response describes a representative sample for this survey?

A. Imani plans to survey 40 people at school, the park, the hospital and a grocery store.

B. Imani plans to survey 100 people from her 7th grade class.

C. Imani plans to survey the 8 members of her family.

D. Imani plans to survey 50 people who attend a school play.

(7.SP.A.1)

29. Eight out of 10 students in a school were successful on the state writing assessment. In Mrs. Johnson's class, 89% of the students were successful on the state writing assessment. Is Mrs. Johnson's data a representative sample? Explain your reasoning.

____

____

____

(7.SP.A.1)

30. The data in this bar graph shows the different sports played by the students in Ms. David's class.

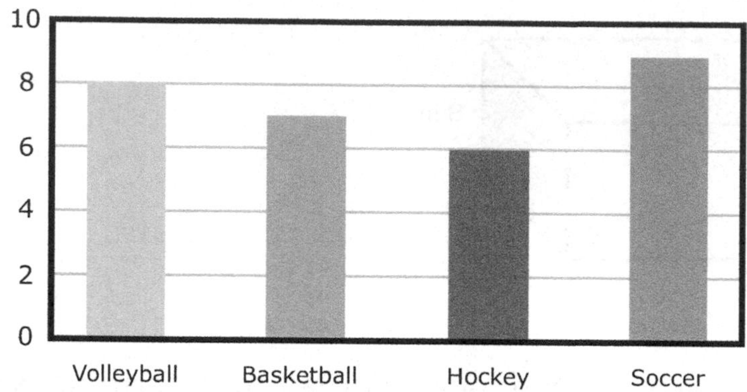

There are 345 students in Ms. David's school. Using this data to make inferences about the entire school, how many students play soccer or volleyball?

A. 28 **B.** 17 **C.** 196 **D.** 300

7.SP.A.2

31. This table shows the number of male and female flamingos at 5 different city zoos.

Male Flamingos	Female Flamingos
10	16
12	18
5	9
7	11
9	14

Using this data, in a larger zoo population of 80 flamingos approximately how many are male?

____

7.SP.A.2

32. These dot plots show the weight of the alligators living in two zoos.

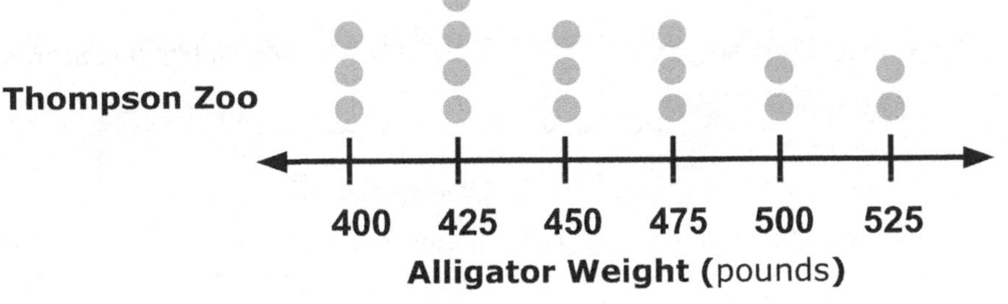

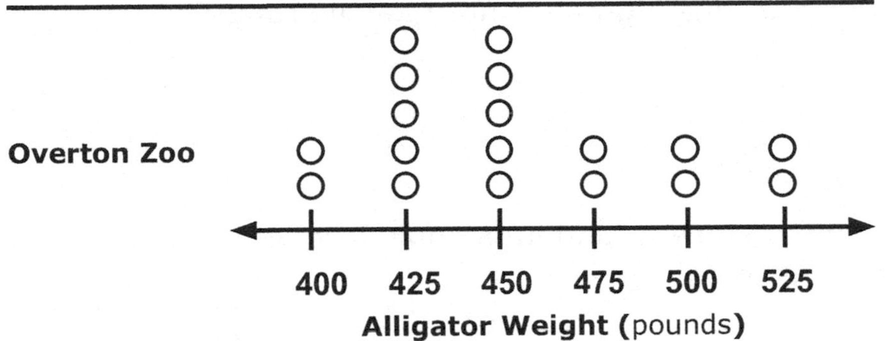

How does the median value of Thompson Zoo compare to the median value of Overton Zoo?

A. The median of Thompson Zoo is 25 lbs. greater than the median of Overton Zoo.

B. The median of Thompson Zoo is 25 lbs. less than the median of Overton Zoo.

C. The median for both dot plots is 450 lbs.

D. The median for both dot plots is 400 lbs.

7.SP.B.3

33. These box plots display the test scores of students in Mr. Quame's and Mr. Field's classes.

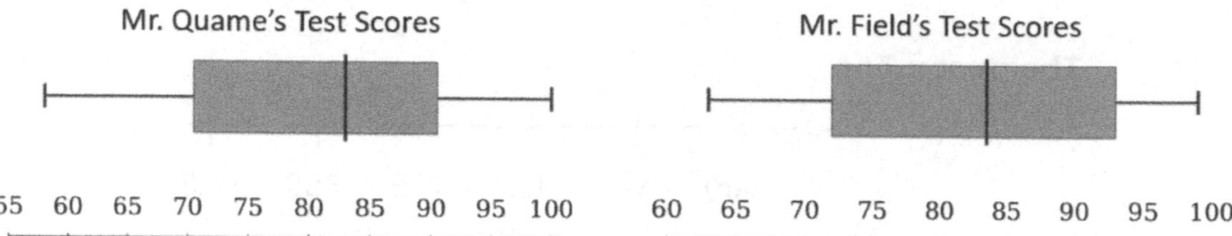

Which box plot has a greater interquartile range?

____

(7.SP.B.3)

34. This dot plots show a random sample of 8 student test scores on two different tests.

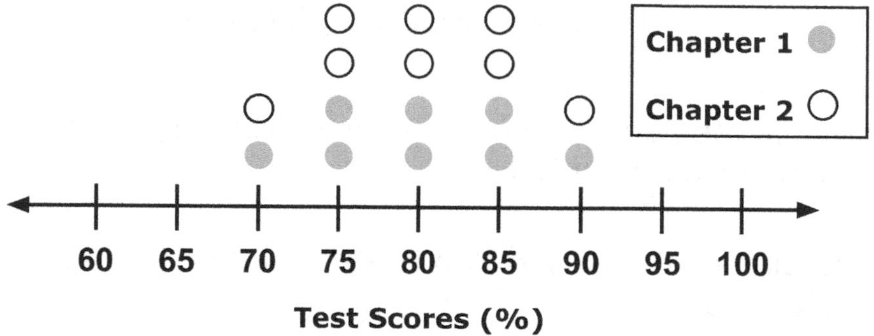

What can you infer based on this data?

A. One-fourth of the class scored below 70% on both tests.

B. The mean score for both tests is approximately 80%.

C. One-fourth of the class scored above 90% on both tests.

D. The range in scores for both tests is 40%.

(7.SP.B.4)

35. Tomas conducts two random surveys to determine how many days each week the people in his neighborhood exercise. The results of his surveys are shown in this table.

Sample A	Sample B
Days of Exercise	Days of Exercise
2	4
3	4
4	5
6	2
7	7
5	6

The range of Sample A is ______________ the range of Sample B.

(7.SP.B.4)

36. The point shown on this number line represents the probability of an event.

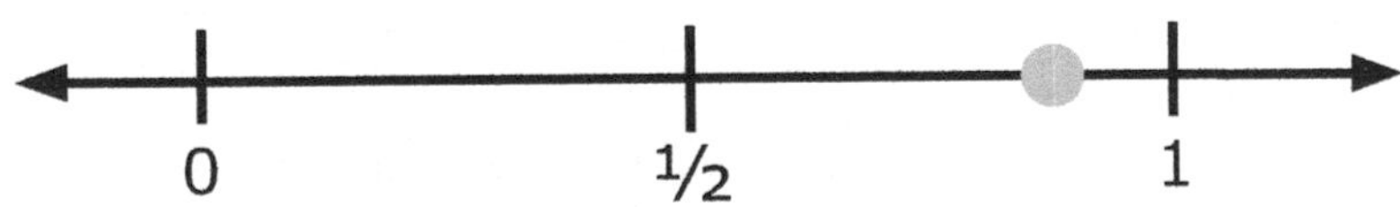

Which statement best describes the event?

A. The event is likely to occur.

B. The event is certain to occur.

C. The event will not occur.

D. The likelihood that event will occur or will not occur is the same.

(7.SP.C.5)

37. The point shown on this number line represents the probability of an event.

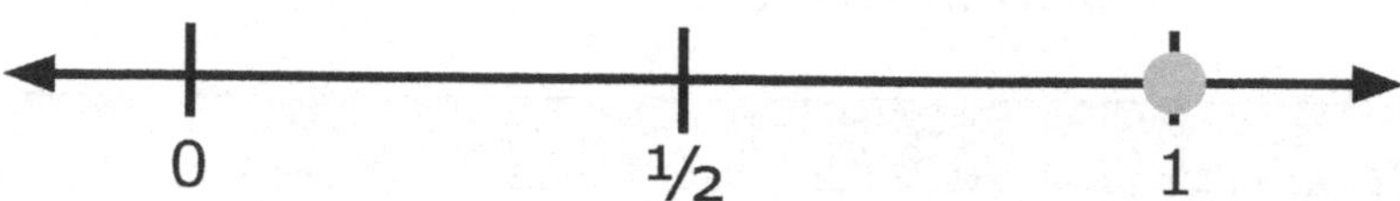

Which statement best describes the event?

A. The event is likely to occur.
B. The event is certain to occur.
C. The event will not occur.
D. The likelihood that event will occur or will not occur is the same.

(7.SP.C.5)

38. A box contains 12 cards. Each card is marked with the numbers 1 through 12. What is the theoretical probability of drawing a card marked with an even number?

____

____

____

(7.SP.C.5)

39. Alex flips a fair coin. The coin has heads on one side, and tails on the other. Alex flips the coin 54 times. She lands on heads 22 times and tails 32 times.

Which value is a prediction of the number of times the coin will land on heads if it is flipped 80 times?

A. 25 **B.** 33 **C.** 40 **D.** 65

(7.SP.C.6)

40. Haley flips 2 coins. Each coin has heads on one side, and tails on the other. Haley flips both coins 50 times.

Which value is an accurate prediction of the number of times Haley should expect to have both coins land heads up?

A. 13 **B.** 25 **C.** 40 **D.** 50

(7.SP.C.6)

41. The chance for snow over a 7-day period is 20%. If the temperature and weather conditions remain the same, how many days will snowfall be predicted over a 21-day period?

____

(7.SP.C.6)

42. Elise has a jar with 9 green marbles, and 11 blue marbles.

Which probability model can be used to determine the chance of Elisa selecting a green marble?

A. $P(green) = \frac{9}{11}$ **B.** $P(green) = \frac{9}{20}$

C. $P(green) = \frac{20}{9}$ **D.** $P(green) = \frac{20}{11}$

(7.SP.C.7)

43. Franklin has a jar with 5 white marbles, 12 green marbles, 7 red marbles, and 6 blue marbles. He uses this model to determine the theoretical probability of selecting each marble.

Marble Color	White	Green	Red	Blue
Probability	$\frac{1}{6}$	$\frac{2}{5}$	$\frac{7}{30}$	$\frac{1}{5}$

...question 43. continued next page

Franklin draws and replaces a marble from the jar 10 times. He finds $\frac{6}{10}$ of these draws result in selecting a white marble.

Which statement could explain this discrepancy?

A. The probability of drawing a white marble from the jar is greater than drawing any other marble.

B. There are more white marbles than green, red, or blue marbles in the jar.

C. The probability of drawing a white marble is misrepresented in the model.

D. The white marbles were probably drawn and replaced from the same location in the jar.

7.SP.C.7

44. Luis and his family are deciding which movies to see this month. They plan to see one movie each weekend for 4 weeks. Luis writes down the names of 7 movies, each on a separate piece of paper. He then places the pieces of paper in a jar for his family members to select 4 movies at random.

How many movie combinations are possible?

A. 14 **B.** 28 **C.** 35 **D.** 16

7.SP.C.8

45. A veterinarian is developing the patient schedule for next week. There are 5 animals to be added to the schedule. In how many different orders could the animals be added to the schedule?

____

7.SP.C.8

ASSESSMENT ②

NAME: .... DATE: ....

COMPREHENSIVE ASSESSMENTS

ASSESSMENT 2

1. A skydiver falls 750 feet in 3 seconds. How many feet does the skydiver fall in 60 seconds?

____

7.RP.A.1

2. One gallon of paint covers 300 square feet of wall space. What equation can be used to find the number of gallons needed to cover 1,050 square feet?

____

7.RP.A.2

3. A recipe requires 3 cups of flour to make 48 cookies. What equation can be used to find the number of cups of flour needed to make 80 cookies?

____

7.RP.A.2

4. Mr. Walz estimated 360 people would attend the middle school holiday concert. The number of people who attended the concert was 15% greater than he expected. How many people attended the concert?

A. 375 **B.** 414 **C.** 345 **D.** 300

7.RP.A.3

5. Eleanor grew 48 plants with 4 seed packets. Next year, she wants to grow 132 plants. How many seed packets should she purchase next year?

____

7.RP.A.3

6. The highest mountain in California is Mount Whitney, with an elevation of 14,505 feet. The lowest point in California is the Badwater Basin at −282 feet. What is the difference, in feet, between these two elevations?

____

7.NS.A.1

7. Paul dove into a pool from 15 feet, above ground level, to a depth of 9 feet in the pool. What's the total vertical distance he dove?

____

7.NS.A.1

8. The value of Curt's investment decreased $450 in 5 months. Which number represents his average investment return each month?

A. $2250 **B.** −$2250 **C.** $90 **D.** −$90

7.NS.A.2

9. If $x = -\frac{3}{8}$ and $y = \frac{4}{6}$, what is $-2xy$?

____

7.NS.A.2

10. A city starts with a population of 52,000. After 25 years, the population is approximately 48,000. How much is the population decreasing each year?

____

7.NS.A.3

11. Translate this statement into an algebraic expression:

The sum of two and five times a number divided by the sum of three times the same number and five.

____

(7.EE.A.1)

12. Kina uses this strategy to simplify an expression.

$$14x + 2(6 + 3x)$$

"First, I would use the distributive property to simplify the terms inside parentheses."

$$14x + 2(6 + 3x)$$

"Next, I would multiply."

$$14x + 2(6) + 2(3x)$$
$$14x + 12 + 6x$$

"Last, I would combine like terms."

$$20x + 12$$

Do you agree with Kina's strategy? Explain your reasoning.

____

____

____

____

(7.EE.A.1)

13. Which expression best represents the perimeter of an equilateral triangle whose side lengths are $\frac{2}{3}x + \frac{1}{6}$ inches?

A. $3\frac{2}{3}x + 3\frac{1}{6}$ inches

B. $\frac{6}{9}x + \frac{3}{18}$ inches

C. $2x + \frac{1}{2}$ inches

D. $\frac{15}{6}x$ inches

7.EE.A.2

14. Hattie is using 10 gallons of water to prepare lemonade for a party. The lemonade recipe states that for every quart of water, she should add $\frac{1}{8}$ cup of lemon juice and $\frac{1}{4}$ cup of sugar.

How much sugar does Hattie need?

A. 40.25 cups **B.** 1 cups **C.** 10 cups **D.** 2.5 cups

7.EE.B.3

15. Roni is arranging pictures in the pages of this book.

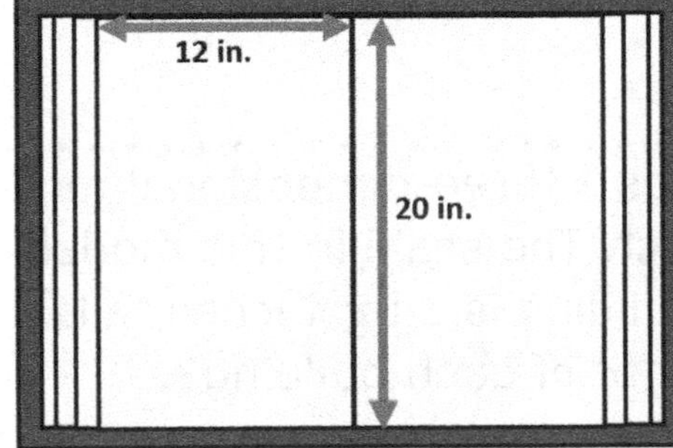

Each picture is 4 inches by 6 inches. What is the maximum number of pictures that will fit on each page of the scrapbook? Explain your reasoning.

____

____

____

7.EE.B.4

ASSESSMENT 2

16. This model is a scale drawing of Cassandra's bedroom.

Dresser
1.25 in.
Bed
Desk
Door

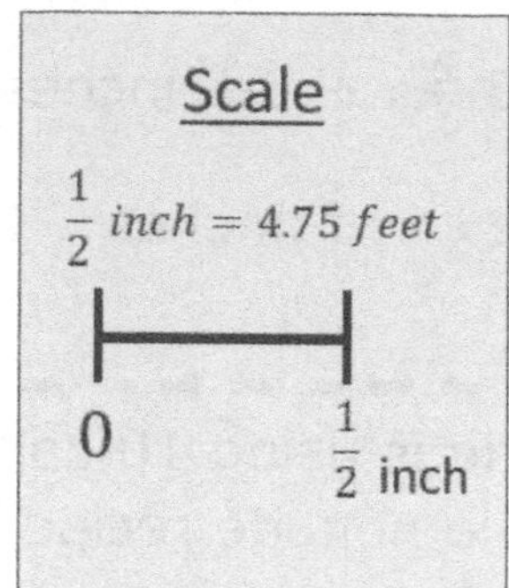

Which equation can be used to find x, the number of feet between Cassandra's bed and her dresser?

A. $4.75(1.25)$

B. $2(4.75)(1.25)$

C. $4.75 + 1.25$

D. $(0.5)(4.75) + (1.25)$

(7.G.A.1)

17. An architect creates a three-dimensional model of a building for a construction project. The scale in this model is 1 inch equals 20 feet. The model building is $14\frac{3}{8}$ inches tall. How would you determine the height of each building?

____

____

____

____

(7.G.A.1)

18. Which set of side lengths will produce a triangle?

Set A	Set B	Set C
5 inches 7 inches 13 inches	6 inches 7 inches 1 inch	3 inches 9 inches 8 inches

____

(7.G.A.2)

19. Which set of side lengths will produce a triangle?

Set A	Set B	Set C
4 inches 9 inches 13 inches	5 inches 5 inches 8 inches	2 inches 3 inches 6 inches

____

(7.G.A.2)

20. Lamont cuts a cross section of a 12-sided prism. His cross section is perpendicular to the base of the prism.

What shape does Lamont create?

A. dodecagon

B. decagon

C. octagon

D. rectangle

(7.G.A.3)

ASSESSMENT 2

21. Ichiro slices this three-dimensional solid vertically from one corner to the opposite corner.

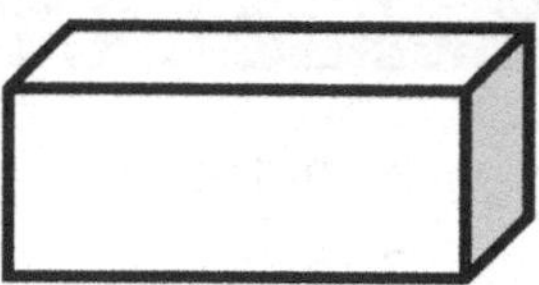

He believes he will create a parallelogram. Do you agree with Ichiro? Explain why.

____

____

____

(7.G.A.3)

22. Evan estimates that the circumference of this lid is 235.5 millimeters.

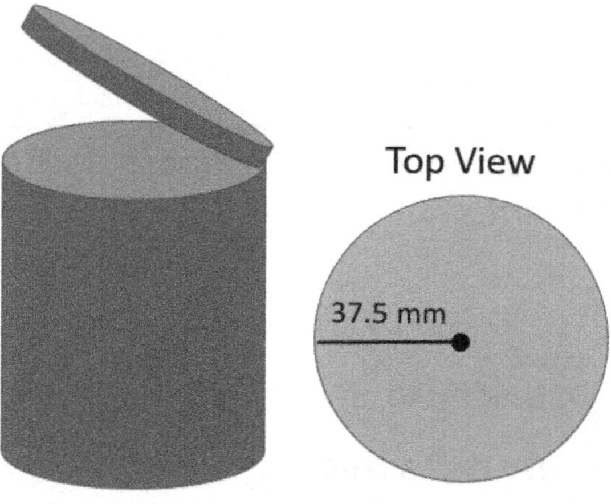

Which expression justifies his estimation?

A. 3.14 (radius)

B. 3.14 (diameter)

C. $3.14(\text{radius})^2$

D. $3.14(\text{diameter})^2$

(7.G.B.4)

23. Chan Ming uses this web camera with his 17-inch computer.

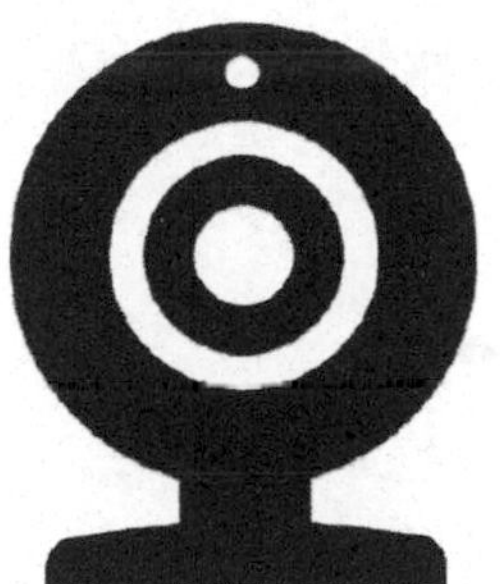

The width of the web camera is $\frac{1}{9}$ the width of his computer. Could a 2-inch cube-shaped box be used to package for this web camera? Explain your reasoning.

____

____

____

(7.G.B.4)

24. What is the measure, in degrees, of $\angle FEG$? Show your work.

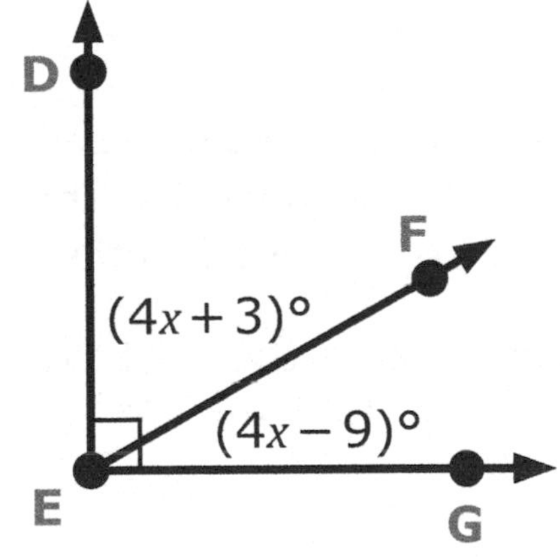

____

____

____

(7.G.B.5)

25. What are the values of a and b? Show your work.

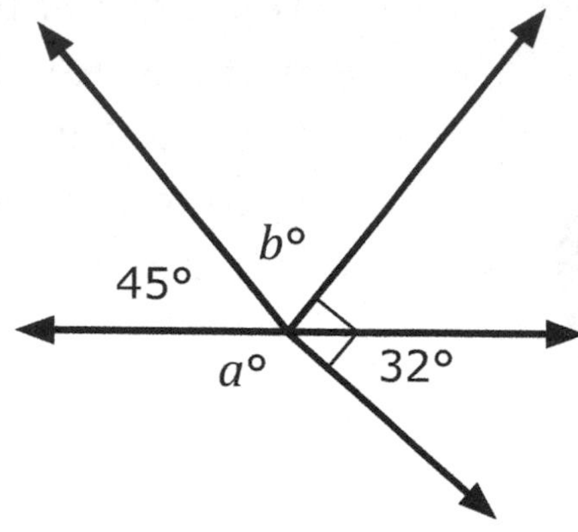

____

____

____

(7.G.B.5)

26. James fills $\frac{3}{4}$ of his toy box with blocks. The height of the toy box is 12 inches, and each block has side lengths of 3 inches.

James places 144 blocks inside the toy box. What is the area, in square inches, of the base of his toy box?

____

(7.G.B.6)

27. What is the surface area of this triangular prism?

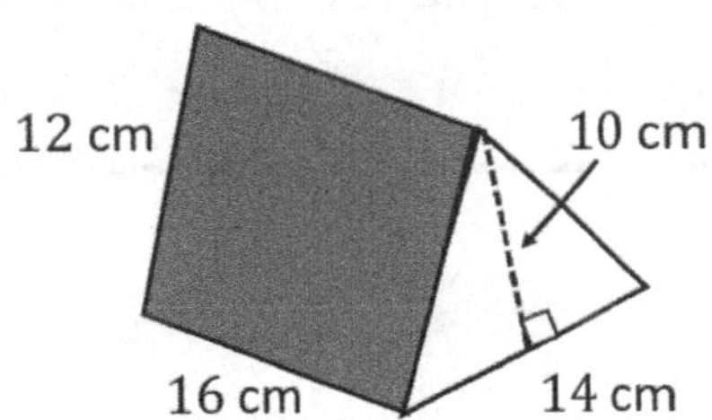

A. $262\,cm^2$ **B.** $748\,cm^2$ **C.** $524\,cm^2$ **D.** $332\,cm^2$

(7.G.B.6)

28. New York City has a population of 8.5 million people. Mr. Goff predicts $\frac{5}{8}$ of the population between the ages of 10 and 18 living in New York City have been to a baseball or basketball game.

Which response could represent a sample size Mr. Goff used to make this prediction?

A. 20 out of 20 people surveyed

B. 50 out 100 people surveyed

C. 80 out of 400 people surveyed

D. 65 out of 100 people surveyed

(7.SP.A.1)

29. Melissa wants to determine how many people in her city voted for a new law. The population of her city if 125,000.

She collects data by asking the first 15 individuals she meets at the mall to complete a survey she created.

Is Melissa's sample representative of the general population?

____

(7.SP.A.1)

30. There are 121 students in Bryson's grade. The data in this bar graph shows the different sports played by the students in his grade.

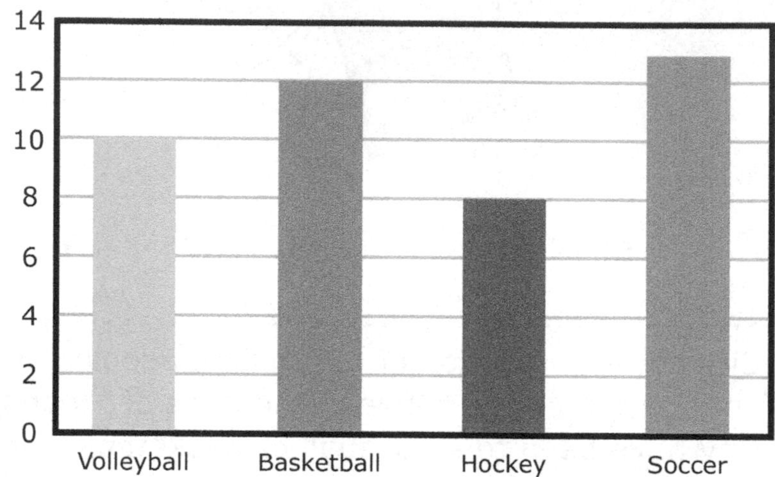

There are 575 students in Bryson's school. Using this data to make inferences about the entire school, how many students play hockey?

A. 38 **B.** 48 **C.** 57 **D.** 62

7.SP.A.2

31. This table shows the number of male and female flamingos at 5 different city zoos.

Male Flamingos	10	12	5	7	9
Female Flamingos	16	18	9	11	14

Using this data, in a larger zoo population of 80 flamingos approximately how many are male?

____

7.SP.A.2

32. These dot plots show the weight of the alligators living in two zoos.

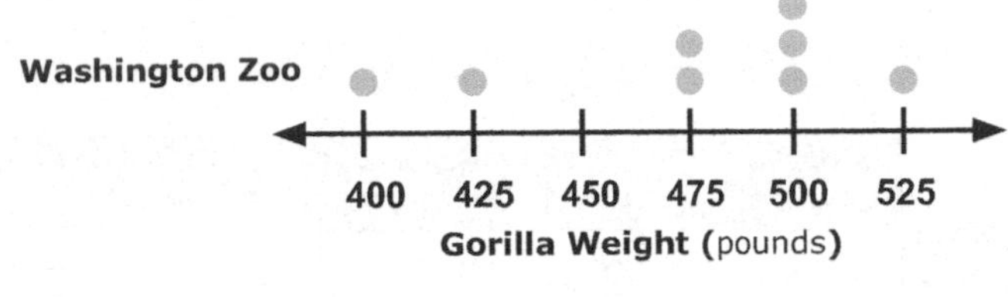

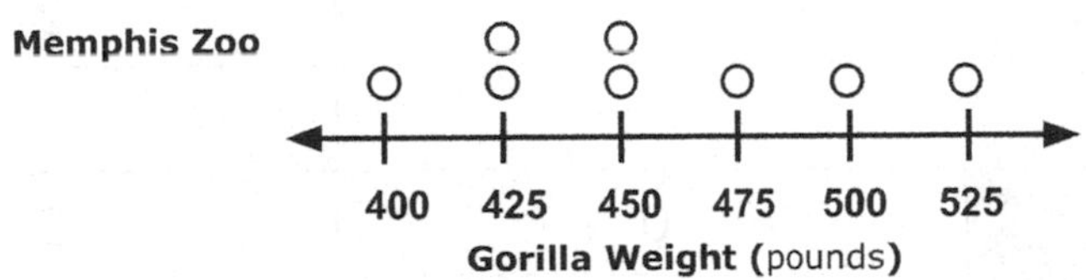

Which statement correctly compares the spread of the dot plots?

A. The spread of the Washington Zoo data is 500 lbs.

B. The spread of the Memphis Zoo data is 25 lbs.

C. The spread of the Washington Zoo is 25 lbs. greater than the spread of the Memphis Zoo data.

D. The spread of both dot plots is the same.

(7.SP.B.3)

33. These box plots compare the test scores of students in two classes.

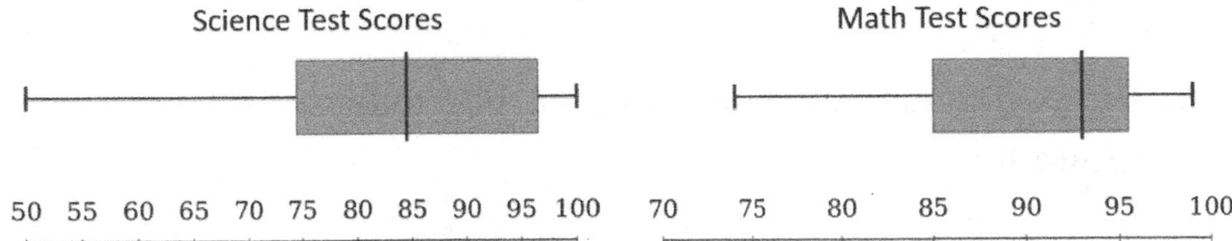

Which box plot has a greater median?

____

(7.SP.B.3)

34. Mrs. Brians asks two groups of coworkers how many sick days they use each year. The data in this table is a random sample of her results.

	Group A	Group B
Number of Sick Days Used	2	3
	3	3
	1	2
	0	2
	0	3
	1	4
	2	2

What can you infer about Mrs. Brians' coworkers based on this data?

A. Most of the coworkers in Group A use more sick days that those in Group B.

B. Most of the coworkers in Group B will take 3 sick days each year.

C. The coworkers in Group A are likely to take more than 3 sick days each year.

D. The coworkers in Group B use more sick days than those in Group A.

7.SP.B.4

35. Felipe conducts two random surveys to determine how many days each week the people in his neighborhood exercise. The results of his surveys are shown in this table.

	Days of Exercise					
Sample A	0	2	1	1	1	2
Sample B	1	0	0	3	5	0

The mean of Sample A is ____________ the mean of Sample B.

7.SP.B.4

36. Saheed flips 3 coins. Each coin has 2 sides — heads and tails. What is the probability that the coins will land with at least 1 tails up?

A. unlikely **B.** likely

C. equally likely and unlikely **D.** certain

7.SP.C.5

37. A box contains 12 cards. Each card is marked with the numbers 1 through 12. What is the probability of drawing a card marked with a 3?

____

7.SP.C.5

38. A box contains 12 cards. Each card is marked with the numbers 1 through 12. What is the probability of drawing a card marked with a number greater than 2?

____

7.SP.C.5

39. Vincent has a bag of marbles. There are 14 yellow marbles in the bag. If the bag contains 50 marbles, what is the experimental probability a marble Vincent draws out of the bag will be yellow?

A. $\frac{50}{14}$ **B.** $\frac{1}{14}$ **C.** $\frac{1}{50}$ **D.** $\frac{7}{25}$

(7.SP.C.6)

40. The chance for rain over 30 days is 30%. If the temperature and weather conditions remain the same, how many days should rain be predicted over 90 days?

____

(7.SP.C.6)

41. The chance for rain over a 7-day period is 30%. The chance of snow is 15% during this same amount of time. If the temperature and weather conditions remain the same, how many days should rain or snowfall be predicted over 14 days? Do not round your answer.

____

(7.SP.C.6)

42. Elaine is randomly selecting a person from her class to work in her group. She uses this probability model to determine the chance of selecting a girl.

$$P(girl) = \frac{5}{12}$$

Which response could describe Elaine's sample space?

A. There are 10 boys in a class of 24 students.
B. There are 7 girls in a class of 12 students.
C. There are 14 boys in a class of 24 students.
D. There are 5 girls in a class of 24 students.

(7.SP.C.7)

43. Three students randomly select colored cubes from a bag. The bag contains 3 different color cubes. Each time a cube is selected, it is returned to the bag. The students' data is recorded in this table.

Results		
Tyrell	**Imogene**	**Samantha**
green	black	green
black	black	white
white	green	green
white	white	black
white	green	green
black	white	green
black	white	black
green	black	white
white	white	white
green	green	white

Based on the outcomes, approximately how many white cubes are in the bag if there are 30 cubes in the bag?

____

7.SP.C.7

44. Nigeal and her friends are making cookies. They need to add flour, white sugar, brown sugar, baking powder, and eggs to a bowl. In how many different orders can Nigeal add these ingredients to the bowl?

A. 10 **B.** 120 **C.** 50 **D.** 150

7.SP.C.8

Ace Academic Publishing
ACHIEVING EXCELLENCE TOGETHER

45. A jar contains 2 red beads, 6 green beads and 2 blue beads. What is the probability of selecting a blue bead, replacing it, and then selecting a green bead?

____

(7.SP.C.8)

ANSWERS AND EXPLANATIONS

Ratios & Proportional Relationships:
Unit Rates and Measurements 240
Proportional Relationships 241
Ratios and Percentages 242
Chapter Review 243
Extra Practice 244

The Number System:
Add and Subtract Rational Numbers 245
Multiply and Divide Rational Numbers 246
Operations with Rational Numbers 247
Chapter Review 248
Extra Practice 249

Expressions and Equations:
Equivalent expressions 250
Expressions and Equations Word Problems 251
Construct Equations and Solve Word Problems 253
Chapter Review 254
Extra Practice 255

Geometry:
Draw and Understand Geometric Figures 257
Area, Surface Area, and Volume 258
Angle Pairs 259
Chapter Review 261
Extra Practice 262

Statistics and Probability:
Understanding Random Sampling 263
Compare and Infer Two Populations 264
Probability Models 266
Chapter Review 267
Extra Practice 268

Assessment 1 269

Assessment 2 272

RATIOS & PROPORTIONAL RELATIONSHIPS: UNIT 1 - UNIT RATES AND MEASUREMENTS

1 Answer: A

Explanation: The unit rate is a comparison between two quantities, with one quantity equal to 1.

2 Answer: C

Explanation: When discussing cost, the unit rate is the cost of one item.

3 Answer: D

Explanation: If the price of milk is $5.92 for 4 gallons, divide $5.92 by 4 to get the price per gallon.

4 Answer: B

Explanation: The questions states that $2\frac{1}{2}$ donuts cost $8.10. Thus, 30 donuts cost $8.10. To find the cost for 1 donut, divide $8.10 by 30.

5 Answer: A

Explanation: If 13 sandwiches cost $78 dollars, then each sandwiches costs $6. To find the cost of 18 sandwiches, multiply 18 and $6.

6 Answer: C

Explanation: To find the unit rate, divide $9.96 by 3 to get the cost per gallon.

7 Answer: D

Explanation: To determine miles per hour, divide 348 miles by 6 hours.

8 Answer: B

Explanation: Divide the prices by the quantities. Target's unit price is the lowest. The unit rate for 8.10 divided by 18 equals $0.45 per ounce.

9 Answer: B

Explanation: Divide 360 by 22.4 and round to the nearest whole number.

10 Answer: C

Explanation: If she drives $\frac{1}{2}$ of the way between two cities in $\frac{3}{4}$ of an hour, then it takes her twice that amount of time to drive the whole way.

11 Answer: B

Explanation: The pack of 6 cans has a unit price of $0.665 (which rounds to $0.67 per can) and the pack of 12 cans has a unit price of $0.6875 (which rounds to $0.69).

12 Answer: A

Explanation: If the unit price is $2.79, multiply by 5 to get the price for 5 gallons.

13 Answer: D

Explanation: If 1 batch of the recipe calls for 2 eggs, then 3 batches of the recipe calls for 2×3, or 6 eggs.

14 Answer: B

Explanation: One dozen cookies requires 0.625 cups of flour ($2.5 \div 4$), to get the amount for 10 dozen ($12 \times 10 = 120$), multiply $0.625 \times 10 = 6.25$.

15 Answer: B

Explanation: The cost for 1 gallon is a unit rate of $6.60 which is more than $3.25 per 1 half-gallon, which has a unit rate of $6.50 per gallon.

16 Answer: $1.25

Explanation: If 8 ft costs $10, to find the cost for 1 foot, divide 8 by 10.

17 Answer: 6

Explanation: If $\frac{3}{4}$ gallon of paint covers half a wall, double that quantity to paint one wall. Then, multiply by 4 to paint 4 walls.

18 Answer: 1 cup brown sugar and 2 sticks of butter

Explanation: Since the number of cookies is 4 times the original recipe, multiply each ingredient by 4, as well.

19 Answer: 4

Explanation: If they walk $\frac{1}{2}$ mile in 15 minutes, then in 1 hour, they walk $\frac{1}{2} \times 4$. Then, multiply by 2 to find the distance they walk in 2 hours.

20 Answer: 18

Explanation: The amount of flour needed for 6 dozen cookies is triple the amount of flour needed for 2 dozen cookies.
$(6 \times 3 = 18)$

RATIOS & PROPORTIONAL RELATIONSHIPS: UNIT 2 - PROPORTIONAL RELATIONSHIPS

1 Answer: B

Explanation: Divide the price by the number of ounces for each brand. Brand B costs $0.0546 per ounce and has the lowest price per ounce.

2 Answer: A

Explanation: Car B has a mileage of 22 miles per gallon $(374 \div 17)$, which is lower than 23.7 miles per gallon.

3 Answer: A

Explanation: Each y-value in the table is 3 times the x-value.

4 Answer: C

Explanation: This equation represents a relationship, where each y-value is $\frac{1}{3}$ of the x-value. The constant is the coefficient of x.

5 Answer: D

Explanation: This equation represents a relationship, where each y-value is 2 times the x-value. The constant is the coefficient of x.

6 Answer: C

Explanation: If she charges $7 per hour, multiply her rate by 2.5 hours, 7×2.5.

7 Answer: D

Explanation: The constant of proportionality is the slope of the graph. Alternatively, choose a point from each graph. The relationship between the x- and y-values should be $y = \frac{3}{4}x$.

8 Answer: B

Explanation: Each y-value should be 3 times as large as the x-value.

9 Answer: A

Explanation: His hair grows $\frac{1}{4}$ inch every 2 weeks so it will take 14 weeks to grow $1\frac{3}{4}$ inches.

10 Answer: C

Explanation: The graph shows a relationship of around $y = 20x$. It will take $5000 \div 20$ minutes to fill the pool. This gives 250 minutes or about 4 $(250 \div 60)$ hours.

11 Answer: B

Explanation: This is a square with equal sides. The constant of proportionality in this relationship is 1.

12 Answer: D

Explanation: The relationship between the number of children and the number of candy bars varies. Thus, there is no constant relationship.

13 Answer: A

Explanation: Cross multiply: $3y = 3 \times 25$. Then divide both sides by 3.

14 Answer: A

Explanation: Multiply both sides by 7. Then, simplify $7 \times 12 \div 28$, resulting in 3.

15 Answer: B

Explanation: Each y-value is four times the x-value.

16 Answer:

x	y
1	5
4	20
9	45

Explanation: To calculate each y-value, you multiply the x-value by the constant of proportionality.

17 Answer: $y=15x$

Explanation: If the constant of proportionality is 15, each x-value is multiplied by 15 to calculate the y-value.

18 Answer: $\frac{1}{2}$

Explanation: Any point of the graph shows that y is one-half the value of x. Thus, the equation is $y = \frac{1}{2}x$.

19 Answer: $\frac{1}{4}$

Explanation: Each y-value is $\frac{1}{4}$ the x-value.

20 Answer: 11.75

Explanation: Divide the number of pages in the book by the number of pages she reads in 1 hour.

RATIOS & PROPORTIONAL RELATIONSHIPS: UNIT 3 - RATIOS AND PERCENTAGES

1 Answer: C

Explanation: To calculate the interest, multiply 200 by 0.04.

2 Answer: D

Explanation: To calculate the interest, multiply 1500 by 0.09.

3 Answer: B

Explanation: To calculate the sales tax, multiply 16 by 0.05. Then, add the tax to the original amount.

4 Answer: C

Explanation: Calculate the tax by finding 3% of 20 , which is 0.60. The total price is $20.60.

5 Answer: C

Explanation: She will make $12.50 from selling 50 cups (50×0.25).Then, subtract the cost of the supplies ($5).

6 Answer: B

Explanation: To calculate the discount, multiply 42×0.15. Then, subtract the result from the original price. Alternatively, calculate the discounted price 85% (100% – 15%) of the original price. Multiply 0.85 by 42.

7 Answer: A

Explanation: When multiplying by a percent, convert the percentage to decimal or fraction form. Then, multiply.

8 Answer: B

Explanation: Solve this problem using the following proportion, where x is the percent: $\frac{48}{50} = \frac{x}{100}$.

9 Answer: B

Explanation: Solve this problem using the following proportion, where x is the percent: $\frac{10}{950} = \frac{x}{100}$.

10 Answer: B

Explanation: To calculate the tip, multiply 35×0.15.

11 Answer: B

Explanation: To figure the realtor's commission, multiply $200{,}000 \times 0.05$.

12 Answer: A

Explanation: To find the price of the home, divide $4800 \div 0.04$.

13 Answer: C

Explanation: To find this year's class size, multiply 680×1.05.

14 Answer: B

Explanation: Calculate his raise, which is $0.04 \times 65{,}000$. Then add the result to his original salary. Alternatively, calculate the new salary as 105% of the original salary, by multiplying $1.05 \times 65{,}000$.

15 Answer: D

Explanation: Calculate the discounted price by multiplying 450×0.85.

16 Answer: 4%

Explanation: You can use the proportion, where X is the percent: $\frac{8}{200} = \frac{X}{100}$. Cross multiply and solve for X.

17 Answer: $0.88

Explanation: If sales tax is 6%, sales tax on his grocery bill of $48 is be $2.88 ($48 \times 0.06$). The groceries will cost $50.88.

18 Answer: $65

Explanation: If the cost with tax is $70.20, divide the total by 1.08 to determine the original cost.

19 Answer: $7.49

Explanation: To calculate the new cost, multiply 49.95×0.15.

20 Answer: $12.60

Explanation: To calculate the tip, multiply: 84×0.15.

RATIOS & PROPORTIONAL RELATIONSHIPS: CHAPTER REVIEW

1 Answer: A

Explanation: The unit cost for the 18-ounce box is $0.255 ($4.59 \div 18$). This is less than the other unit cost.

2 Answer: D

Explanation: He will use 3 gallons to paint his room. Multiply 24×3.

3 Answer: D

Explanation: If she saved $39 in 3 months, she saves $13 per month. Divide 195 by 13.

4 Answer: A

Explanation: To find the unit price, divide the cost by the number of apples. The lowest unit cost is the best.

5 Answer: B

Explanation: To calculate the miles per gallon, divide the total number of miles by the gallons of gas used.

6 Answer: 4

Explanation: Multiply the amount for one serving by 8.

7 Answer: $\frac{3}{4}$

Explanation: She made 6 smoothies (5 friends and herself). Divide the total amount of juice by the number of smoothies.

8 Answer: D

Explanation: The constant is the slope, and the relationship between x and y. Based on points on the graph, $y = 10x$.

9 Answer: A

Explanation: If she jogs 3 miles in 45 minutes, then her rate is 15 minutes every mile.

10 Answer: B

Explanation: If 15 postcards cost $11.25, then 1 postcard costs $0.75.

11 Answer: C

Explanation: Write and solve al proportion comparing two ratios of miles to gallons.

12 Answer: $16

Explanation: According to the graph, when $x = 4$, $y = 16$. The graph is that of the equation $y = 4x$.

13 Answer: 120

Explanation: Multiply the length of each practice by the number of nights he practices.

14 Answer: 3

Explanation: Cross multiply the proportion; $4x = 12$. Then, divide by 4.

15 Answer: D

Explanation: The current population is 92% (100% − 8%) of what it was 20 years ago. The population of the town 20 years ago can be determined by the equation $0.92x = 320{,}000$.

16 Answer: $18,000

Explanation: To calculate the commission, multiply: 450000×0.04.

17 Answer: 12

Explanation: Use proportion: $\frac{3}{15} = \frac{x}{60}$. Cross multiply.

18 Answer: 18

Explanation: One way to solve this problem is to multiply: 15×1.2

19 Answer: 798

Explanation: To calculate Mumia's points, multiply Shawn's points by 0.76.

20 Answer: 21%

Explanation: To calculate percent change, subtract the actual value from the original value. Then, divide that quotient by the original value.

RATIOS & PROPORTIONAL RELATIONSHIPS: EXTRA PRACTICE

1 Answer: D

Explanation: Andelle packs 25 barrels in an hour. Jonathan packs 24 barrels in an hour. The difference is 1.

2 Answer: C

Explanation: To determine the unit rate, divide the miles traveled by the number of gallons of gas used.

3 Answer: $0.01

Explanation: There are 128 fl. oz. in 1 gallon. Kevin pays $0.03 per ounce for the orange juice. The 6-pack contains 72 oz. of orange juice. Linda pays $0.04 per ounce for the orange juice.

4 Answer: $1\frac{5}{16}$ of $\frac{21}{16}$

Explanation: There are 24 cookies in 2 dozen cookies. Use the proportion equating two ratios of brown sugar to cookies to find the answer.

5 Answer: 35

Explanation: Using the ratio ($\frac{1}{3}$) miles: ($2\frac{1}{3}$) minutes, Jamal runs 1 mile in 7 minutes. Multiply 7 by 5 to determine how many minutes it will take him to run 5 miles.

6 Answer: Brea

Explanation: Multiply Jacki's distance and time by 2nd divide by 3. She runs 800 meters in 4 minutes and 12 seconds. Brea runs 800 meters in 2 minutes and 30 seconds. Brea runs faster.

7 Answer: 42

Explanation: There were 16 games last season and 32 games this season with a total of 48 games in both seasons; $\frac{7}{8}$ of 48 is 42.

8 Answer: $y = \frac{4}{5}x$

Explanation: Each y-value is $\frac{4}{5}$ of each x-value. The constant of proportionality is $\frac{4}{5}$.

9 Answer: No

Explanation: The equation representing the graph is $y = 3x$. Every y-value is 3 times as large as every x-value.

10 Answer: 1

Explanation: Solve for y by dividing both sides by 4. The equation is written as $y = x$. The constant of proportionality is 1.

11 Answer: 20

Explanation: The cost of potatoes is $1.50 per pound. Divide 30 by $1.50.

12 Answer: B

Explanation: The constant of proportionality is 15.8. Divide 662.81 by 15.8.

13 Answer: They both paid the same amount of money per gallon.

Explanation: Linda spent $4.79 per gallon. Erica spent $19.16 on 4 gallons, so she also spent $4.79 per gallon.

14 Answer: Cups 1 and 3

Explanation: The ratio of red paint to yellow paint used in Cups 1 and 3 is the same.

15 Answer: C

Explanation: The population increased by 8% to 1,668 (1,544 × 1.08) students, then decreased from this amount by 2%. Multiply 98% (100 - 2%) by 1,668 resulting in 1,634.

16 Answer: A

Explanation: Working backwards, multiply the population for each year by 98.25% or 0.9825 five times until you get to the population for 2004.

17 Answer: 70

Explanation: Steve spends $61.75 on the jersey and a total of $66.07 including the service fee. $66.07 is 69.55% of $95.

18 Answer: 24

Explanation: The original monthly savings amount is $62.50. The cost of the computer reduces to $330, after he saved $187.50. For the last 3 months, he needs to save $47.50 each month. This is a 24% decrease from $62.50.

19 Answer: $108.65

Explanation: The sales tax rate is 8.65%

20 Answer: $4.18

Explanation: The cost of one pizza this year is $4.33. If the cost increased by 3.6%, divide $4.33 by 1.036. The original cost was $4.18.

THE NUMBER SYSTEM: UNIT 1 - ADD AND SUBTRACT RATIONAL NUMBERS

1 Answer: D

Explanation: The absolute value of −8 is 8. The absolute value of − 8 + 0 is also 8.

2 Answer: C

Explanation: Add 9 to − 16 to determine the sum. Absolute value changes the negative value to a positive value.

3 Answer: D

Explanation: Adding − 15 + 42 is the same as subtracting 42 − 15.

4 Answer: B

Explanation: To represent this problem on a number line, start at − 8 and move 5 units to the right to − 3.

5 Answer: A

Explanation: The model on the number line, starts at − 3 and moves 6 units to the left to − 9. This is equivalent to − 3 − 9.

6 Answer: A

Explanation: To solve, change subtracting a negative, which is called a "double negative" to adding a positive. Then, add 75 and 37.

7 Answer: B

Explanation: To combine a percent and a decimal, change the percent to decimal form by multiplying it by 0.01.

8 Answer: C

Explanation: First, subtracting a negative is equivalent to adding a positive so the expression is an addition problem. Convert the fraction to decimal form. Then, add the two numbers.

9 Answer: D

Explanation: When adding a positive number using a number line, move the initial value to the right, in a positive direction.

10 Answer: C

Explanation: To solve for x, add 6 to both sides, (add -11 to 6).

11 Answer: A

Explanation: To get a value of 12 on the right side, subtract 5 from 17, which means add $17 + -5$.

12 Answer: B

Explanation: Adding a negative number is the same as subtracting a positive number.

13 Answer: D

Explanation: Subtracting 14 from 7 means $7 - 14$ or $7 + -14$, which results in -7.

14 Answer: A

Explanation: When subtracting a positive number from any other number, on the number line, move to the left by the value of the number being subtracted.

15 Answer: D

Explanation: Another way to rewrite this problem is subtract from the positive number.

16 Answer: C

Explanation: Calculate his total weight change, with $7 + 4 - 15$.

17 Answer: $-12, 8, |-9|, 12, |-18|$

Explanation: Simplify $|-18|$ and $|-9|$ to 18 and 9. Then, order the numbers from smallest to largest.

18 Answer: 9 degrees

Explanation: To calculate, add $|-4|+5$. Absolute value of -4 is 4, $4+5=9$.

19 Answer: 15

Explanation: To calculate, multiply 6×3, and then add 3×-1.

20 Answer: 10

Explanation: To calculate, add $|-4|+6$. Absolute value of -4 is 4, $4+6=10$.

THE NUMBER SYSTEM: UNIT 2 - MULTIPLY AND DIVIDE RATIONAL NUMBERS

1 Answer: C

Explanation: Divide 5.9375 by 4.75.

2 Answer: B

Explanation: Subtract $3\frac{1}{2}$ from 21. Then, divide the result by 21.

3 Answer: C

Explanation: To calculate, multiply 25 by 0.72.

4 Answer: A

Explanation: Any number divided by 0 is undefined.

5 Answer: C

Explanation: When dividing one fraction by another fraction,change the division to multiplication, multiplying by the reciprocal of the second fraction.

6 Answer: B

Explanation: When dividing one fraction by another fraction,change the division to multiplication, multiplying by the reciprocal of the second fraction.

7 Answer: D

Explanation: When dividing one fraction by another fraction, change the division to multiplication, multiplying by the reciprocal of the second fraction.

8 Answer: A

Explanation: A negative number divided by another negative number becomes a positive number.

9 Answer: A

Explanation: When dividing a fraction by an integer, keep fraction the same, change to multiplying by the reciprocal of the second number, so 3 becomes $\frac{1}{3}$.

10 Answer: B

Explanation: Each pair of negatives cancel, so the expression changes to $4 \times 4 \times 4 \times 4$, which is 256.

11 Answer: C

Explanation: The two negatives cancel. Then to find the product, $\frac{1}{3} \times \frac{1}{3}$, multiply the numerators and multiply the denominators.

12 Answer: D

Explanation: A negative number times a negative number is always positive.

13 Answer: C

Explanation: A positive number divided by a negative number is always a negative number.

14 Answer: C

Explanation: When multiplying two fractions, multiply the numerators and multiply the denominators.

15 Answer: B

Explanation: $12\frac{1}{3}$ becomes $\frac{37}{3}$. Then multiply the numerators and multiply the denominators. Cross cancel whenever possible.

16 Answer: – 40

Explanation: To calculate, divide $-320 \div 8$. The result is a negative value because it is a loss of population.

17 Answer: $4\frac{1}{2}$ or 4.5

Explanation: Multiply $6 \times \frac{3}{4}$.

18 Answer: 2

Explanation: Based on the rate given, the dog digs 1 ft/hour so it will take the dog 2 hours.

19 Answer: $136

Explanation: Divide 680 by 5.

20 Answer: – 950

Explanation: Divide −3800 by 4. The value is negative because the elevation is decreasing.

THE NUMBER SYSTEM: UNIT 3 - OPERATIONS WITH RATIONAL NUMBERS

1 Answer: B

Explanation: To calculate the new temperature, subtract $-17 - 6$, which is equivalent to $-17 + -6$.

2 Answer: C

Explanation: Calculate with $|-6|+14$ or $14 - (-6)$, which changes to $14 + 6$.

3 Answer: D

Explanation: Add $-950+375$.

4 Answer: B

Explanation: Subtract 250 from 625.

5 Answer: B

Explanation: Calculate the eagle's final elevation by combining: $42+144 - 126$.

6 Answer: D

Explanation: Determine the final elevation by combining: $425+63 - 100$.

7 Answer: D

Explanation: To divide fractions, keep the first term the same. Then change the division to multiplication, and multiply by the reciprocal of the second term.

8 Answer: A

Explanation: When multiplying a negative number by a positive number, the result is a negative number.

9 Answer: A

Explanation: The statement is never true because, on the left side of his equation, the absolute value of any number is always positive, and, on the right side of his equation, the opposite of an absolute value of any number is always negative.

10 Answer: C

Explanation: To calculate the new balance, start with the beginning balance, add the deposit and subtract the bills which were paid from the account: 487.59 + 289.56 − 198.67 − 323.10 = 255.38

11 Answer: A

Explanation: Add the time from B.C. (500) to the time in A.D. (1886).

12 Answer: 23

Explanation: Subtract 1994 − 1971.

13 Answer: D

Explanation: Divide −75 by 3.

14 Answer: A

Explanation: Subtract 27,985 − 5(1,750).

15 Answer: 16

Explanation: Combine: 19 − 7+4.

16 Answer: 38

Explanation: She answered 21 questions correctly and 4 incorrectly. To calculate her score, multiply 21 by 2 and then subtract 4.

17 Answer: 98.8

Explanation: Subtract 101.8 − 3.

18 Answer: 7.5 minutes

Explanation: Divide 180÷24.

19 Answer: − 7

Explanation: Subtract 6 − 13.

20 Answer: $1

Explanation: To find the balance, start with the beginning balance, add the deposit, and subtract the check: 82 + 45 − 96.

THE NUMBER SYSTEM: CHAPTER REVIEW

1 Answer: D

Explanation: To calculate the number of cars, combine 89 − 60 − 23 + 28.

2 Answer: A

Explanation: Surface level is 0 m. If Liam's depth is 0 − 12 or −12 m below the water, then Morgan is −12 + 5.3 m below the water.

3 Answer: B

Explanation: The expression $n - m = -3 - (-5) = -3 + 5 = 2$.

4 Answer: A

Explanation: The expression $= -b - a = -(-9) - (-6) = 9 + 6 = 15$.

5 Answer: C

Explanation: Rewrite this problem as 48 − 23.

6 Answer: $31

Explanation: Subtract 189 − 220 = −31. He owes the bank $31 because the result is negative.

7 Answer: D

Explanation: Multiply the numerators and multiply the denominators in the product $\frac{5}{8} \times \frac{1}{2}$.

8 Answer: A

Explanation: The negative sign of a fraction can be in the numerator, in the denominator, or in front of the fraction bar.

9 Answer: A

Explanation: The given expression is simplified with the following steps: $(-9 \div 3) + \frac{1}{2}(-8 - 2) = (-3) + \frac{1}{2}(-10) = -3 + -5 = -8$

10 Answer: D

Explanation: The given expression is simplified with the following steps:
$(\frac{3}{4} \times 12) + (-9 \div 3) - 2\frac{1}{8} =$
$(9) + (-3) - 2\frac{1}{8} = 9 - 3 - 2\frac{1}{8} = 3\frac{7}{8}$.

11 Answer: $205\frac{1}{2}$ or 205.5

Explanation: Calculate:
$300 - 6(15\frac{3}{4}) = 300 - 94.5 = 205.5$.

12 Answer: − $3.75

Explanation: Subtract 62.25 from 84.75. Divide the difference by 6.

13 Answer: B

Explanation: First, convert 80 minutes to $1\frac{1}{3}$ hours. Then, multiply −380 by the number of hours. Since he is descending the mountain elevation change is negative.

14 Answer: C

Explanation: Multiply $-4 \times 2\frac{1}{2}$.

15 Answer: D

Explanation: Add $|-2| + 39$.The resulting amount is negative because the temperature has fallen.

16 Answer: A

Explanation: To divide fractions, keep the first term the same. Then change the division to multiplication and multiply by the reciprocal of the second term.

17 Answer: A

Explanation: Multiply the quantity by the unit price. Eli spent more. He spent $2.76. Peyton spent $2.44.

18 Answer: $30\frac{2}{3}$ seconds

Explanation: Divide $23 \div 0.75$.

19 Answer: 50 degrees

Explanation: Add the two values using an absolute value: $|-18| + 32$.

20 Answer: 20,519 feet

Explanation: Combine the two elevations using subtraction: $20{,}237 - (-282)$.

THE NUMBER SYSTEM: EXTRA PRACTICE

1 Answer: C

Explanation: The second number is $12\frac{2}{3}$ units to the right of $-4\frac{2}{3}$, which means add $12\frac{2}{3}$ to $-4\frac{2}{3}$.

2 Answer: A

Explanation: The distance between 60 and 12 is 48. Three-fourths ($\frac{3}{4}$) of 48 is 36. Point Y is at $12 + 36 = 48$.

3 Answer: D

Explanation: Subtracting a positive integer is the same as adding a negative integer.

4 Answer: $320

Explanation: Determine the amount of money in Sarah's bank account by working backwards using this expression:
$382 + 85 - 147$.

5 Answer:

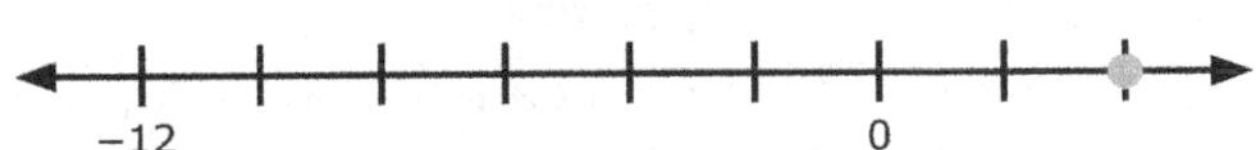

Explanation: The expression $2(-4 + 8 - 2)$ equals 4. Each hash mark on the number line is 2 units.

6 Answer: −1

Explanation: Point R is on −15 on the number line. Fourteen units greater than −15 is −1.

7 Answer: Convert the fraction to a decimal or convert the decimals to fractions, then add/subtract.

Explanation: Rewrite the expression $-0.75 + (-\frac{1}{8}) + 2.25$ as $-0.75 + (-0.125) + 2.25$. Then add and subtract. The result is 2.05 or $2\frac{5}{100}$.

8 Answer: No

Explanation: The fraction $\frac{4}{9}$ is equivalent to 4 divided by 9 or 4 divided by 3 times one-third.

9 Answer:

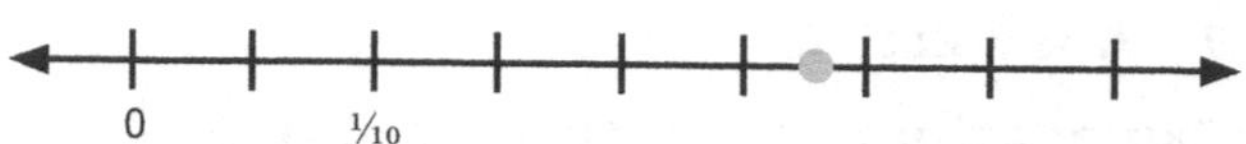

Explanation: The decimal represents $\frac{3}{11}$. The fraction $\frac{3}{11}$ is between $\frac{2}{10}$ and $\frac{3}{10}$ on the number line because 0.2727 is between 0.2 and 0.3 on the number line.

10 Answer: $m < 0$

Explanation: If $-m + 2m < 0$, then combine the like terms on the left side which results in $m < 0$.

11 Answer: No

Explanation: Some fractions with a denominator of 9, such as $\frac{9}{9}$, $\frac{18}{9}$ and $\frac{27}{9}$ are whole numbers or terminating decimals.

12 Answer: 4.8 or $4\frac{4}{5}$ or $\frac{24}{5}$

Explanation: Rewrite the expression as $\frac{(-4)}{7} \times \frac{21}{8} \times (-3\frac{1}{5})$. Change the mixed number to an improper fraction: $\frac{(-4)}{7} \times \frac{21}{8} \times (-\frac{16}{5})$. Cross cancel and multiply the remaining fractions.

13 Answer: $\frac{2}{5}$

Explanation: To determine the value of x, work backwards: divide $-11\frac{11}{20}$ by -3, subtract $\frac{15}{4}$ and multiply by 4.

14 Answer: Yes

Explanation: The fraction $\frac{1}{4}$ is equivalent to 0.25. The original fraction is 0.825/0.25. Multiply the numerator and the denominator by 1,000 to eliminate the decimals and the result is 825/250.

15 Answer: 6 × 0.15 or 0.9

Explanation: The distance between each unit in the graph is 0.15 miles. The school and the grocery store are 6 units apart.

16 Answer: $63

Explanation: Altogether Cecil and his friends earn $210 (4 × 17.50 × 3). After spending $21 on supplies, there is $189 left. Divide by 3.

17 Answer: $\frac{1}{3} \times -\frac{5}{4} \times \frac{5}{2}$

Explanation: Dividing by a fraction is equivalent to multiplying by its reciprocal.

18 Answer: $0.54

Explanation: The cost of the grapes is $3.33 (2.25 × 1.48). The cost of the apples is $2.79 (2.25 × 1.24).

19 Answer: $5.73

Explanation: The cost of the bananas is $1.11 (1.625 × 0.68), and the cost of the strawberries is $4.62 (3 × 1.54).

20 Answer: 70 cm

Explanation: The width of the rectangle is $23\frac{1}{3}$ cm. The perimeter is $2(23\frac{1}{3} + 11\frac{2}{3})$.

EXPRESSIONS AND EQUATIONS: UNIT 1 - EQUIVALENT EXPRESSIONS

1 Answer: B

Explanation: Combine the terms $4x$, $3x$, and $-2x$ because they are like terms.

2 Answer: C

Explanation: Using the distributive property, multiply each term inside the first set of parentheses by 3.

3 Answer: A

Explanation: Subtracting $9x$ from $4x$ is a correct first step because both terms have the same variable. They are like terms.

4 Answer: C

Explanation: Henri is following correct order of operations.

5 Answer: C

Explanation: There are 2 sides with a

length of 45 ft., 2 sides with a length of 72 ft., and one side with with a length of 103. The expression 2(45 + 72) simplifies the total value of the first 4 sides. Adding the expression to 103 represents the rest perimeter of the playground.

6 Answer: A

Explanation: The second triangle has sides that are 3 ft. longer than the first triangle. Add 3 to the lengths of each side to determine the perimeter of the second triangle.

7 Answer: B

Explanation: Simplify the expression inside the bracket: $[8 + 4(5\frac{1}{2})]$, $[8 + 22]$, becomes 30. The expression becomes $\frac{1}{5} \times (30)$.

8 Answer: B

Explanation: Order of operations dictates multiplying and and dividing in order from left to right. In the expression, division comes first.

9 Answer: A

Explanation: The area formula of a triangle is $A = (bh)/2$. The length of the base (b) is $8\frac{2}{3}$ cm. The height of the triangle (h) is $15\frac{1}{8}$ cm.

10 Answer: $3x+3$

Explanation: Combine like terms resulting in $3x + 3$.

11 Answer: D

Explanation: Find the length of each side by dividing each term in the perimeter by 4.

12 Answer: C

Explanation: Find the length of each side by dividing each term in the perimeter by 4.

13 Answer: D

Explanation: A square has 4 equal sides, so the length of each side is the perimeter divided by 4.

14 Answer: A

Explanation: Combine like terms: $10x + 5x = 15x$. The entire distance is $15x + 25$. Find halfway around the building by multiplying this distance by $\frac{1}{2}$ or dividing it by 2.

15 Answer: B

Explanation: Combine like terms: $27x - 12x = 15x$ The length of the rope is $30 + 15x$. Divide this length by 3.

16 Answer: C

Explanation: The expression is the result of adding the cost of the item $(100\%x)$ to the sales tax on the item $(8.25\%)(x)$.

17 Answer: A

Explanation: The total cost of the item m is added to the tax (0.0945m).

18 Answer: B

Explanation: Sales tax on the item in Louisiana is $0.0891x$ in decimal form. Sales tax on the item in Texas is $0.0825x$ in decimal form. The difference is $0.0066x$.

19 Answer: D

Explanation: The sales tax is 8.89%, which is 0.0889 as a decimal. Find the total cost by adding the original cost ($8.89) to the sales tax (0.0889×8.89).

20 Answer: C

Explanation: The decimal 0.125 represents an interest rate of 12.5%

EXPRESSIONS AND EQUATIONS: UNIT 2 - EXPRESSIONS AND EQUATIONS WORD PROBLEMS

1 Answer: C

Explanation: Subtract the bills from the beginning balance in the account: $215 - 57 - 125 - 32 - 91 = x$; $x = -90$.

2 Answer: A

Explanation: The cost of the pants and hat is 19 + 19 or $38. Subtract this amount from the total spent: 85 – 38 = 47.
Then, divide by 2: 47/2 = 23.5.
The shirts cost $23.50 each.

3 Answer: B

Explanation: The total of the bills is $368.30 (62.15 + 142.70 + 84.95 + 77.50). Add 368.0 to the ending balance of $125.03 after the bills were paid.

4 Answer: C

Explanation: Add the cost of 4 shirts and 2 pair of socks: (4 × 21.99 + 2 × 4.75 = 97.46) Subtract this 97.46 from 135.04: 135.04 - 97.46 = 37.58

5 Answer: B

Explanation: Subtract $95 from $706.94, and divide the difference by 42.

6 Answer: D

Explanation: Subtracting 112 from 595.84 gives the balance Lamont needs to pay over 18 months. To find the monthly payment divide that balance (595.84 – 112) by 18.

7 Answer: 12

Explanation: Simplify the expression using correct order of operations. The first step is subtracting the terms within parentheses. Then multiplying the result by 6. The last step is to subtract 24.

8 Answer: A

Explanation: Subtract 18 from −3:
−3 - 18 = −21. The temperature at 9pm was −21 degrees. Next, add 22 to −21:
22 + −21 = 1. The temperature at 5pm was 1 degree Fahrenheit.

9 Answer: C

Explanation: The temperature decreased 2 degrees each hour for 9 hours. This is a temperature change of 18 degrees. Working backwards, add 18 to −11: −11 + 18 = 7 The temperature at 6 pm the previous day was 7 degrees Fahrenheit.

10 Answer: D

Explanation: There are 3 hands, and he spends 2.6 hours building each of them:
3 × 2.6 = 7.8 Subtract 7.8 hours from 184.2 hours: 184.2 - 7.8 = 176.4 hours

11 Answer: B

Explanation: One-third of 78 is 26. There are 26 Wild Roses. One sixth of 78 is 13. There are 13 Old Garden Roses. The remaining roses, [78 - (26+13)], are Modern Garden Roses. There are 39 Modern Garden Roses.

12 Answer: 2.77

Explanation: Simplify the expression using the order of operations. The first step is combining the numbers within parentheses. Remove the second parenthesis. Then divide. Lastly, add and subtract.

13 Answer: 693

Explanation: Multiply 8 times 126, and 2.5 times 126. Subtract the two results.

14 Answer: 935

Explanation: Calculate the distance between the office and cafeteria ($\frac{748}{4}$ = 187 ft.). Add the result to the distance between the cafeteria and band hall (748 ft.).

15 Answer: 1,122

Explanation: Multiply 13 times 132, and 4.5 times 132. Subtract the two results.

16 Answer: 464

Explanation: Calculate the distance between the office and band hall ($\frac{696}{6}$ = 116ft.). Next, calculate the distance between the office and cafeteria (696 × $\frac{5}{6}$ = 580ft.).Subtract the two results.

17 Answer: $104.50

Explanation: Calculate $\frac{1}{2}$ of 319 ($159.50), and subtract this value from $319, leaving her $159.50. Next, subtract $55 which was placed in the bank. (159.50 – 55 = 104.50). She spent $104.50 on clothes.

18 Answer: 940

Explanation: Use order of operations to find each total. The estimate is 21,210, and the actual answer is 22,150. The difference between these two results is 940.

19 Answer: 220

Explanation: Using compatible numbers and rounding to determine 20% Estimate that there are 400 sixth graders, 300 seventh graders, and 400 eighth graders. Multiply each quantity by 0.2 and add the results.

20 Answer: 10 and 11

Explanation: Of the 40 players, $\frac{1}{4}$ of them are from the Caribbean, so 10 are from the Caribbean ($\frac{40}{4}$ = 10). Next, 19 of them are Americans. The remaining players (40 − 10 − 19 = 11) are from Central America.

EXPRESSIONS AND EQUATIONS: UNIT 3 - CONSTRUCT EQUATIONS AND SOLVE WORD PROBLEMS

1 Answer: B

Explanation: The expression shows the cost of a small pizza ($10) and 2 medium pizzas ($18 × 2) with sales tax (1.0845) and the $1.99 discount off the entire order.

2 Answer: C

Explanation: The equation shows the cost of buying a salad with 5 toppings (5 × 0.50) and a drink, and the sales tax that is added to the cost.

3 Answer: D

Explanation: There are 5 people (Khalid and his friends). Together they must walk at least 100 miles (greater than or equal to). They have already walked 12 miles.

4 Answer: A

Explanation: The inequality uses the greater than or equal to symbol because Riley must meet a goal of at least $500. The expression 20$y$ represents how much Riley will raise each week.

5 Answer: C

Explanation: The 30 represents the money raised already during the fundraiser because it is added to her weekly goal.

6 Answer: D

Explanation: One student will sit at a desk and 5 students can sit at a table. The expression 10 + 5m represents 10 students at the 10 desks and 5 students each at m tables. This expression equals the number of students in the class and equals 35 because there are 35 students in the class.

7 Answer: A

Explanation: Subtract the number of students seated at square tables (3 × 4) from the number of students (28) and divide this difference by 8 to get the number of round tables needed.

8 Answer: A

Explanation: Multiply the time it takes the chemical to dissolve by the rate at which it dissolves: 15.4 × 1.025 = 15.785.

9 Answer: B

Explanation: Divide the weight of the chemical by the rate at which it dissolves.

10 Answer: 17.5x + 125 = 650

Explanation: The amount of money already saved (125) is added to the amount of money to be saved each week (17.5x).

11 Answer: 37.3 + 3x ≥ 50

Explanation: He has already hiked 37.3 miles. To calculate how many miles he has to hike during the next 3 days, add 37.3 to 3x in the inequality: 37.3 + 3x ≥ 50.

12 Answer: 5x+2.5 ≥ 15

Explanation: After Yesenia has already ran 2.5 miles. She will run 5 more days.
The inequality will contain the expression 2.5 + 5x.

13 Answer: 2,866

Explanation: The equation $4.8x = 1,440$ has the solution $x = 300$. Thus, the entire trip is $1,440 + 1\frac{2}{3}(300) + 3(300 + 26 =$ 2,866 miles.

14 Answer: $1,363\frac{2}{3}$

Explanation: Two-thirds of 2,045 is $1,363\frac{2}{3}$.

15 Answer: 18.23 cm and 23.24 cm

Explanation: Use the equation $2L = 46.48$ to determine one dimension. Find the length of the other dimension with this equation: $(82.94 - 46.48)/2$

16 Answer: Answers may vary. $6x+54=180$

Explanation: The graphic shows the figure has 6 equal sides labeled x, and two sides whose lengths are 27 cm.

17 Answer: $3x + 14 = 35$

Explanation: The 3-pound weights must be added to the side with 2 7-pound weights. Both sides of the scale will weigh 35 pounds.

18 Answer: $16 < 85$ $3x + 16 = 85$

Explanation: The 3-pound weights must be added to the side with 4 4-pound weights. Both sides of the scale will weigh 85 pounds.

19 Answer: 52

Explanation: Subtract the number of points she has already collected (195) from the points she needs to advance (1,365). She needs 1,170 more points. Divide 1,170 by 45, which gives 26. Multiply 26 by 2 to get 52 more coins.

20 Answer: No

Explanation: He should express the value of nickels and dimes as 0.05 and 0.10 (in decimal form).

EXPRESSIONS AND EQUATIONS: CHAPTER REVIEW

1 Answer: B

Explanation: Combine like terms:
$5m + 3m + 2m + 2m = 12m$;
$45 + 5 = 50$;
$12m + 50$.

2 Answer: A

Explanation: Translate the word expression to $3(x + 6)$. Simplify the expression, using the distributive property, to $3x + 18$.

3 Answer: C

Explanation: Translate the verbal expression to $7y - (6 + 5y)$. Distribute the negative: $7y - 6 - 5y$. Combine like terms: $7y - 5y = 2y$. $2y - 6$

4 Answer: $90 - 6x$

Explanation: Simplify the expression given as the length of the side: $10 + 4x - (5x - 5) = 10 + 4x - 5x + 5 = 15 - x$. Multiply by 6 because a hexagon has 6 sides: $6(15 - x) = 90 - 6x$. Answers may vary.

5 Answer: $35x - 150$

Explanation: Remove the parentheses: $(3x - 30) + 4x = 3x - 30 + 4x$. Combine like terms: $3x - 30 + 4x = 7x - 30$.
Multiply by 5 because a pentagon has 5 sides: $5(7x - 30) = 35x - 150$. Answers may vary.

6 Answer: $24(3x^2 + 5x + 18)$

Explanation: The greatest common factor of 72, 120, and 432 is 24. Divide each term by 24. The remaining trinomial cannot be factored further.

7 Answer: A

Explanation: The cost of shoes can be represented by this expression: $t + t + t = 3t$.

8 Answer: B

Explanation: The amount of the discount is 7.5% of the price. Multiply 0.075 by p.

9 Answer: No

Explanation: The expression $0.20x$ is the amount of the discount of the original cost. To determine the total cost, she would use the expression $x - 0.20x$ or $0.80x$.

10 Answer: Yes

Explanation: If the discount is 35%, then she will pay 65% of the cost of the items. The total cost can be represented by the given expression or $x - 0.35x$.

11 Answer: $8x + 16 - 2$ or $8x + 14$

Explanation: Distribute and combine like terms.

12 Answer: no

Explanation: The coefficients in the first expression are 98.2, 14, and 1. Since the terms are like terms, combine them by combining the coefficients. The expression 84.2 does not include the term with a coefficient of 1.

13 Answer: C

Explanation: convert each percent to decimal form and multiply by the number of students. Add the results for each grade.

14 Answer: 389

Explanation: The restaurant serves 105 people between 6am and 11am ($21 \times 5 = 105$), 342 people between 11am and 2pm ($2 \times 38 \times 3 = 228$), and 56 people between 2pm and 4pm ($28 \times 2 = 56$).

15 Answer: B

Explanation: There are 324 8th grade students who ride a bus (405×0.80). There are 300 6th grade students who ride a bus (400×0.75). The difference is 24 students.

16 Answer: 4,823

Explanation: The elevation decreases 3,512 feet each day. Subtract 3,512 from the elevation on Wednesday.

17 Answer: C

Explanation: Divide the mass by the amount of time it takes the chemical to dissolve: $36.32/31.04 = 1.17$. The chemical dissolves 1.17 grams per second.

18 Answer: A

Explanation: The closed symbol means the solution is all numbers less than or equal to -2.

19 Answer: 18

Explanation: Solve for x with the equation $101.5 = 2(14.75) + 4x$. The combined length of the 4 missing sides is 72 cm. Divide this length by 4.

20 Answer: Yes

Explanation: He writes an equation correctly representing the vlaue of each coin in decimal form, and the variable relates to the number of pennies needed to have a total of $4.00.

EXPRESSIONS AND EQUATIONS: EXTRA PRACTICE

1 Answer: D

Explanation: Combine like terms: $4\frac{4}{5}x + 1\frac{2}{3}x + 3x = 9\frac{7}{15}x$. Add 26. The answer is $(9\frac{7}{15}x + 26)$ miles.

2 Answer: (8)(6 – 3n) or 48 – 24n

Explanation: The expression can be written in more than one way. The verbal expression "The product of ..." requires the distributive property of multiplication. Then, simplify $8(6-3n)=48-24n$.

3 Answer: A

Explanation: The middle piece of cardboard is represented by x. The longest piece is $3x$. The shortest piece is $x - 12$.

4 Answer: $(15x - 45) + 3x + (10x - 15)$
or
$28x - 60$

Explanation: Write the expression for the sum of the three angles, or combine the like terms from the three expressions given in the diagram: $28x - 60$.

5 Answer: $(\frac{11}{5}x + 110) + (4x - 45) + (2\frac{3}{5}x - 5) + (3x + 5)$
or
$11\frac{4}{5}x + 65$

Explanation: Express the answer as the sum of the angles: $(\frac{11}{5}x + 110) + (4x - 45) + (2\frac{3}{5}x - 5) + (3x + 5)$ or combine like terms from four expressions given in the diagram.

6 Answer: $6[4(2x - 8)]$
or
$6(8x - 32)$
or
$48x - 192$

Explanation: A hexagon has 6 sides. Find the perimeter by multiplying the given expression by 6.

7 Answer: Here is an example: $1.0875\,(4x + 3y)$

Explanation: Add the two costs and multiply by $(1 + 0.0875)$. The total cost of hotdogs and hamburgers can be represented by more than one expression.

8 Answer: $(\frac{9}{2}x) \div 3$
or
$\frac{9/2x}{3}$

Explanation: Divide the expression by. The length of one piece is one-third of $9x(\frac{1}{6})$ or $3x(\frac{1}{3} + \frac{1}{6})$. Answers may vary.

9 Answer: One expression which could represent this situation would be $\frac{20x + 18}{2}$

Explanation: The line segment AB (the distance between Point A and Point B) is the radius. The radius is half of $14x + 18 + 6x$, which is $10x + 9$.

10 Answer: The body temperature increases by 17%.

Explanation: The decimal 1.017m represents the increase in body temperature by 17% over the two day period.

11 Answer: The body temperature decreased by 5% the first day, then increased by 5% the second day.

Explanation: Multiplying the body temperature by 0.95 represents a decrease in temperature by 5%. Multiplying this value by 1.05 represents a 5% increase. The net change over the two days is 0.

12 Answer: yes

Explanation: The coefficients in the first expression are 1, 0.75, and 0.25. Since the terms are all like terms, add the coefficients together.

13 Answer: A

Explanation: Two-fifths of 25 is 10. Subtract $25 - 10 - 13 = 2$. Two players are from the Caribbean islands.

14 Answer: $783.75

Explanation: Add the two fractions together. He will spend $\frac{9}{20}$ of his money, which means he will have $\frac{11}{20}$ of his money remaining in the account. Multiplying this fraction by 1,425 yields the amount of money remaining.

15 Answer: 7,749
above
The values are positive.

Explanation: Compare the elevations each day. The difference is 2,785 feet. Add 2,785 to the value on Tuesday or subtract 2,785 from the value on Thursday.

16 Answer: 24.36
4.64

Explanation: There are 16 ounces in 1 pound. For the dog's weight, multiply the cat's weight by 3. For the bird's weight, divide the cat's weight by 28 and then multiply the answer by 16 to convert to ounces.

17 Answer: B

Explanation: Divide the total amount spent 3 to find the cost of one pizza with sales tax (1.07*x*). Divide by 1.07 to find the price of the pizza before tax is added.

18 Answer: C

Explanation: Divide the number of sheets produced by the number of packages times the number of sheets in each package: 238,000/(42 × 500) = 11.333 hours.

19 Answer: C

Explanation: The formula for the perimeter of a rectangle is: P =2L + 2W. Since the perimeter and length are known, the values 30 and 4 can be substituted into the formula.

20 Answer:

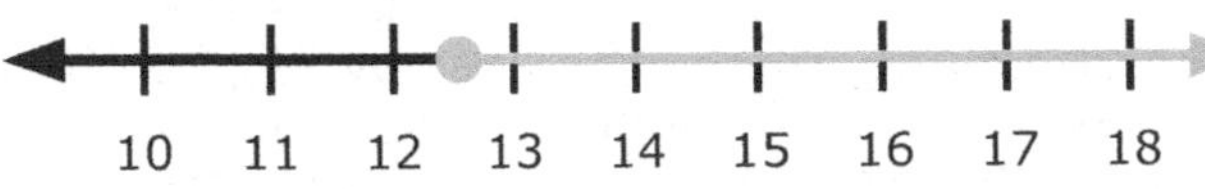

Explanation: The number of miles remaining is 12.5. Yesenia must run at least 12.5 more miles to reach her goal.

GEOMETRY: UNIT 1 - DRAW AND UNDERSTAND GEOMETRIC FIGURES

1 Answer: B

Explanation: Add the number of inches: 2.87 + 2.34 = 5.21 inches. Using the map scale, multiply the number of inches by 337: 5.21 × 337 = 1755.77 or 1756 miles.

2 Answer: C

Explanation: Multiply the number of inches by the scale ratio:
2.28 × 337 = 768.36 miles

3 Answer: D

Explanation: Bismarck, ND, is 1,232 miles from Seattle, Washington.

4 Answer: A

Explanation: Each inch represents 337 miles; multiply 337 by 1.87.

5 Answer: 2.9 inches

Explanation: The height of the Empire State Building is 1,454 feet. Divide 1,454 by 500, which is 1.908. Round the answer as required.

6 Answer: The scale factor is 1.5

Explanation: The proportion $\frac{3}{2} = \frac{4.5}{3}$ shows the relationship between the corresponding sides of the parallelograms. Use the ratios in the proportion to find the scale factor.

7 Answer: 0.8

Explanation: The proportion (2.75)/4 = 2/3.2 shows the relationship between the corresponding sides of the rectangles. Use the ratios in the proportion to find the scale factor.

8 Answer: D

Explanation: The triangle has 2 identical angles, which are 45 degrees, and a 90-degree angle. The triangle also has two sides that have the same length.

9 Answer: C

Explanation: An acute scalene triangle contains three acute angles, all having have different measures.

10 Answer: A

Explanation: An equilateral triangle has 3 congruent angles and 3 congruent sides.

11 Answer: D

Explanation: An obtuse scalene triangle has three angles with different measures,

and one angle's measure is greater than 90 degree.

12 Answer: C

Explanation: The measure of the two angles are 60 degrees 35 degrees.
The measure of the third angle is
180 − (35 + 60) or 85 degrees.

13 Answer: 93 degrees

Explanation: The two angles have measures of 15 degrees 72 degrees.
The measure of the third angle is
180 − (15 + 72) or 93 degrees.

14 Answer: 41 degrees

Explanation: The measure of the obtuse angle in the isosceles triangle is 98 degrees. The other two angles have the same measure. The measures of all three angles add up to 180.
Solve the equation $x + x + 98 = 180$.

15 Answer: Answers may vary

Explanation: In a triangle, the sum of the two shorter sides must be greater than that longest side. The length of the third side must be a whole number greater than 7 inches and less than 18 inches.

16 Answer: B

Explanation: The cross section of a rectangular prism on a plane perpendicular to its base is a rectangle.

17 Answer: D

Explanation: The cross section of a cube sliced parallel to its base is a square.

18 Answer: equilateral triangle

Explanation: The shape is an equilateral triangle because the points are equidistant from each other.

19 Answer: C

Explanation: Slicing a right rectangular pyramid perpendicular to its base creates a triangle or a trapezoid. If the cross section does not pass through the vertex of the pyramid, then it has the shape of a trapezoid.

20 Answer: pentagon

Explanation: A cube sliced through 5 of its 6 faces has a cross section of a pentagon. An example is:

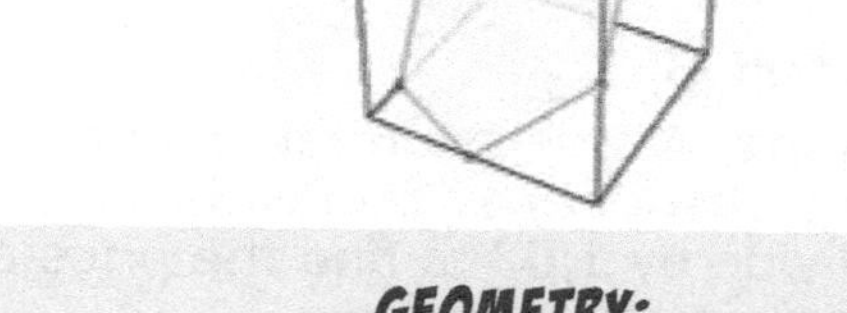

GEOMETRY: UNIT 2 - AREA, SURFACE AREA, AND VOLUME

1 Answer: A

Explanation: The distance is one-half of the the circumference of the pond.
(0.5)(3.14)(2)(25.5).

2 Answer: C

Explanation: The area of the pond is calculated by: (3.14)(29.4)(29.4)

3 Answer: C

Explanation: Using the formula for the area of a circle, divide the area by π (3.14) and take the square root of the result. Multiply this value by 2 to determine the distance across the lake (4.5 miles). Divide the distance by the rate.

4 Answer: B

Explanation: Find the area. Divide the circumference by π (3.14) The diameter of the playground is 65.94/3.14 or 21 yards. Divide the diameter by 2 to find the radius. The radius is 10.5 yards. The area of the playground is (3.14)(10.5)(10.5) or 346.19 sq. yards. Multiply the area by 12:
346.19 × 12 = 4154.28.
The mulch will cost $4,154.

5 Answer: A

Explanation: The circumference of the wheel is 50.24 cm. To find the time it takes the wheel to turn 1 full turn, divide the circumference by the rate. 50.24/22 = 2.28 or 2.3 seconds.

6 Answer: A

Explanation: The area of each donut is (3.14)(2.88)(2.88) or 26 square inches. One donut uses 26 × 0.12 grams of sugar (3.12 grams). Multiply by 24.

7 Answer: 0.5 feet

Explanation: The diameter of the circle is 1 foot. The length of the radius is one-half of the diameter.

8 Answer: $\frac{1}{36}\pi$ or 0.087 square yards

Explanation: The diameter of the circle is $\frac{1}{3}$ of a yard. The length of the radius is $\frac{1}{6}$ of a yard, or one-half of the diameter. Use the formula for the area of a circle.

9 Answer: 3.14:1.

Explanation: Calculate the ratio by dividing the circumference by the diameter.

10 Answer: 6.5:1

Explanation: The area is 530.66 and the circumference is 81.64. The area is 6.5 times the circumference.

11 Answer: C

Explanation: The area of the base is 165 square cm. The height of the prism is 41.25 square cm. The volume is the area the base times the height.

12 Answer: D

Explanation: Solve the equation $3.5(2x) = 42$. The solution is $x = 6$, so the longest side of the base is 12 cm and the height is 11 cm. Calculate the volume by multiplying the length times width times height.

13 Answer: B

Explanation: The base is in the shape of a square and the volume is 81 cubic inches. Thus, the height is 9 inches.

14 Answer: B

Explanation: The volume of a right rectangular prism is calculated by multiplying its length, width, and height.

15 Answer: C

Explanation: The area of the rectangle is 99 square inches. The area of the triangle is 99/2 or 49.5 square inches.

16 Answer: B

Explanation: The volume of Prism A is 665 cubic centimeters (7 × 5 × 19), and the volume of Prism B is 980 cubic centimeters (14 × 7 × 10).

17 Answer: B

Explanation: Polygon A has an area of 12 square inches, but Polygon B has an area of 25 square inches.

18 Answer: A

Explanation: The area of Polygon B is 60.06 cm^2 ((0.5)(15.5/2)(15.5).

19 Answer: No

Explanation: The height of the prism is 19 inches, not 14 inches. This calculations should be $\frac{(16\times12)}{2} \times 19$.

20 Answer: Yes

Explanation: The volume formula of the prism V=Bh. She correctly used the formula for the area of a trapezoid for the area of the base.

GEOMETRY: UNIT 3 - ANGLE PAIRS

1 Answer: D

Explanation: Find the value of b by subtracting the sum of the triangle's other two interior angles [63 and (180 – 82)] from 180.

2 Answer: C

Explanation: Find the value of a by subtracting the sum of the triangle's other two interior angles [23 and (180 – 875)] from 180.

3 Answer: A

Explanation: Since the model shows a right angle, the measures of angles g, c, and d have a sum of 90 degrees. Thus, the relevant part of the straight angle is a right angle. Find the measure of angle g by subtracting 70 from 90.

4 Answer: B

Explanation: Based on the markings in the figure, the 3 angles have a sum of 90 degrees.

5 Answer: C

Explanation: The measure of vertical angles are equal.

6 Answer: A

Explanation: The angles with measures $a, f, c,$ and h have a sum of 180 degrees. Vertical angles involved help show this sum.

7 Answer: C

Explanation: The two angles are supplementary and have a sum of 180 degrees.

8 Answer: C

Explanation: Use the equation $180 = 6x$ to find x. The solution is $x = \frac{180}{6}$.

9 Answer: A

Explanation: The two angles are supplementary and have a combined measure of 180 degrees. Solve the equation $2x + 7 + x + 8 = 180$. The value of x is 55.

10 Answer: B

Explanation: Solve the equation $4x + 9 + 3x - 4 = 180$, $x = 25$, so one angle has a measure of 109 degrees, and the other angle has a measure of 71 degrees.

11 Answer: C

Explanation: Solve the equation $9x - 20 + 3x + 20 = 180$, $x = 15$. The measure of the smallest angle is 65 degrees.

12 Answer: B

Explanation: If $b + c + d = 12$, then $a = 48$. Then since a and e are the measures of vertical angles, each equals 48 degrees. Together they have a combined measure of 96 degrees.

13 Answer: 69

Explanation: From right angle relationships, the value of a is 50, and the value of b 19 degrees.

14 Answer: 205

Explanation: The value of a 140 because of a supplementary relationship. The value of b is 65 because 180 − 50 − 65 = 65.

15 Answer: 63 degrees.

Explanation: The angle with the measure of x degrees is an alternate interior angle to an angle with the measure of 63 degrees. Alternate interior angles have the same measure.

16 Answer: 76

Explanation: The value of a is 128 because of a supplementary angle relationship, and the value of b is 52 because of an alternate interior angle relationship. Subtract the one from the other.

17 Answer: 46 degrees.

Explanation: Write the equation $7x - 3 = 67$. The solution is $x = 10$. This makes $z = 113$ because of supplementary angles. Using vertical angles, $z = 67$. The difference is 46.

18 Answer: Angle CAB: 98 degrees
Angle ACD: 82 degrees
Angle BDC: 75 degrees
Angle ABC: 105 degrees

Explanation: Find the measures of all of the angles using supplementary angles and properties of same side interior angles.

19 Answer: Yes

Explanation: The definition of supplementary angles contains two angles whose measures add up to 180 degrees. Vertical angles are pairs of opposite angles made by intersecting lines. If the vertical angles are right angles, their measures add up to 180 degrees.

20 Answer: No

Explanation: Based on the figure, the two angles are not congruent.

GEOMETRY: CHAPTER REVIEW

1 Answer: B

Explanation: There are 8 half-inches in 4 inches. Each half-inch represents 1/8 mile.

2 Answer: B

Explanation: Find width of the house using this proportion:

$$\frac{1\text{ cm}}{4.5\text{ ft}} = \frac{x}{40\text{ ft}}$$

3 Answer: C

Explanation: Find the length of the classroom using this proportion:

$$\frac{1.5\text{ in.}}{3.75\text{ ft.}} = \frac{x}{24\text{ ft}}$$

4 Answer: C

Explanation: A trapezoid has two pairs of same side interior angles that are supplementary, and add up to 180 degrees.

5 Answer: B

Explanation: A rhombus is a parallelogram with opposite equal acute angles, opposite equal obtuse angles, and four equal sides.

6 Answer: B

Explanation: The given information creates a unique isosceles triangle. Only 1 triangle can be created with these dimensions.

7 Answer: 41 degrees

Explanation: The triangle is obtuse and isosceles, so the measures of angles S and T are both 41 degrees.

8 Answer: C

Explanation: A diagonal cross section in a cone that does not pass through the base creates an ellipse. An example is:

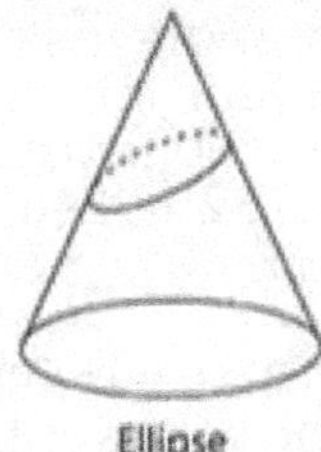

Ellipse

9 Answer: C

Explanation: The image shows a plane slicing from the upper left corner of the prism to the lower right-hand corner.

10 Answer: A

Explanation: The cross-section creates a triangle.

11 Answer: D

Explanation: As long as the cross section is parallel to the base, the cross section in a triangular prism is rectangular.

12 Answer: A

Explanation: The length of the second hand is the same as the length of the radius. Find the radius by dividing the circumference by 2(3.14).

13 Answer: C

Explanation: If the tip of the minute hand rotates 1.57 mm/min, then the circumference of the watch face is 1.57(60) = 94.2 mm. The length of the minute hand is the same as the length of the radius. Find the radius by dividing the circumference by 2(3.14).

14 Answer: $\frac{1}{2}$ inch.

Explanation: Find the length of the radius with the equation π times radius squared = $\frac{\pi}{16}$. The radius is $\frac{1}{4}$ inch. The length of the diameter is twice the length of the radius.

15 Answer: B

Explanation: The unlabeled angle is supplementary to 103 degrees, so it's measure is 77 degrees. The angle with b as its measure is 180 − 77 − 35 = 45 degrees.

16 Answer: C

Explanation: The angle with a measure of a degrees is an angle inside a quadrilateral. The sum of the four interior angles of the quadrilateral is 360 degrees, so $a = 360 - 90 - 52 - 148 = 70$.

17 Answer: 7

Explanation: The sum of the measures of the angles inside a quadrilateral is 360. Solve the equation $(7x - 5) + 108 + 108 + 100 = 360$.

18 Answer: A

Explanation: The shaded area is a parallelogram. The area equals base times height, so $A = 47.75(32) = 1{,}528$ square inches. Divide the area by 100 to find how many $\frac{1}{2}$ pints are needed. The answer is 15.28. Multiply by 2.

19 Answer: C

Explanation: The base of the prism is the triangle. Each triangle has an area of 35 square cm.

20 Answer: 710 cm2

Explanation: The surface area of the box is 2(17)(6) + 2(11)(6) + 2(17)(11).

GEOMETRY: EXTRA PRACTICE

1 Answer: B

Explanation:
Use the proportion $\frac{1 \text{ in}}{100 \text{ ft.}} = \frac{x}{550/2 \text{ ft}}$ to find the height of Ichiro's model, where x is the height of the capital in the model.

2 Answer: 1.5

Explanation: Use the ratio of the larger hexagon's perimeter to the smaller hexagon's perimeter to find the scale factor.

3 Answer: No

Explanation: Divide 3,915 by 800, and round the answer to 5 or round 3,915 to the 1,000 and divide it by 800, which is also 5, not 50. The river would be approximately 5 inches on the map.

4 Answer: C

Explanation: In a triangle, the sum of the lengths of the two shorter sides of the triangle is greater than the length of the third side. Only 1 choice satisfies this requirement. The lengths are 12 in, 10 in, and 14 in.

5 Answer: B

Explanation: Given the lengths of 2 legs and the shared angle, only 1 triangle can be constructed.

6 Answer: D

Explanation: Because of the position and lengths of the given line segments, the measure of Angle D must be an acute angle with a measure less than 50 degrees.

7 Answer: Yes

Explanation: The length of the third side must be greater than the sum of the lengths of the two shorter sides.

8 Answer: A

Explanation: Any cross section parallel to the base of a prism has the same shape as the base of the prism.

9 Answer: A

Explanation: When a cross section is vertical to the base of any prism, the cross section forms a rectangle.

10 Answer: C

Explanation: The triangular pyramid has a triangular base. Slicing this pyramid perpendicular to the base creates a triangle. An example is:

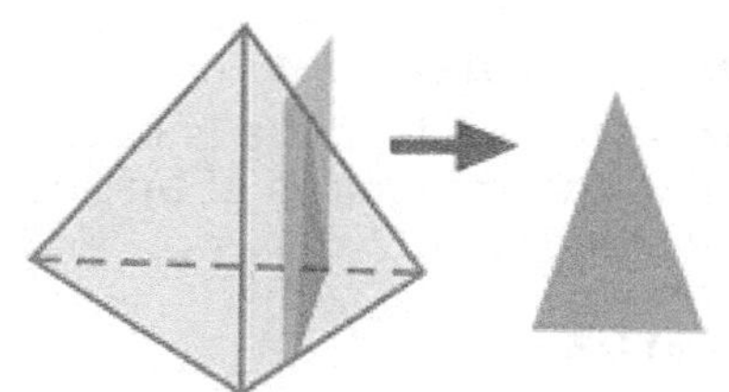

11 Answer: A triangle

Explanation: Slicing any pyramid (or cone) vertically from the vertex forms a triangle.

12 Answer: A

Explanation: The diameter of a quarter is 23.8 mm or 2.38 cm. Thus, one stack of quarters, on edge will fit in the case. To determine how many quarters can fit, divide 144 mm by 1.75 mm.

13 Answer: B

Explanation: The clock has a diameter of 75.36/3.14 inches or 24 inches. If it is centered along the wall, which is 144 inches wide, the center of the clock will be 72 inches from Point A. The radius of the clock is 12 inches, so the distance between Point A and the edge of the clock is 60 inches.

14 Answer: 3.925 inches

Explanation: The width of the web camera is the length of the diameter. The circumference, πd is $\frac{15}{12}$ (3.14) inches.

15 Answer: D

Explanation: The sum of the measures of the angles is 360. One angle is 90 degrees, another angle is labeled only as a degrees, the third angle is vertical to 112 degrees, and the fourth angle is labeled as $3x + 5$.

16 Answer: 45

Explanation: Calculate the value of a by subtracting (108+108+(180 – 81)) from 360.

17 Answer: 21

Explanation: Using knowledge of vertical and supplementary angles, solve the equation $4x - 9 + 5x = 180$. The solution is $x = 21$.

18 Answer: 12 inches

Explanation: The volume of a cube is the length of a side cubed. Find the cube root of 1,728.

19 Answer: C

Explanation: The volume of the prism (l × w × h) is 286 cubic inches, so half of this amount is 143 cubic inches.

20 Answer: C

Explanation: Two triangles each have an area of 59.5 square centimeters. One triangle has an area of 68 square centimeter. Another triangle has an area of 84 square centimeters.

STATISTICS AND PROBABILITY: UNIT 1 - UNDERSTANDING RANDOM SAMPLING

1 Answer: D

Explanation: The survey question immediately cases bias in the survey because the question sets a tone about recycling that will make the students instinctively want to support recycling.

2 Answer: C

Explanation: The sample size is biased because it assumes the population being sampled is mostly women.

3 Answer: B

Explanation: To appropriately represent the number of police officers in the US, the sample size should represent departments in every state.

4 Answer: C

Explanation: The sample is random because it is an unbiased representation of the total population. However, it is a convenience sample.

5 Answer: A

Explanation: The number of students surveyed in the sample represent 8 out of 74. This is approximately 11% of the population.

6 Answer: C

Explanation: The number of students surveyed in the sample represent 42 out

of 74. This is approximately 57% of the population.

7 Answer: C

Explanation: The statistic is the only one based on the entire population of those living in Los Angeles.

8 Answer: Yes

Explanation: The sample size of 20 marbles out of 100 is reasonable. Two out of 20 marbles are green, which is 10%.

9 Answer: No

Explanation: The sample size of 10 out of 40 is a reasonable representation of the marbles in the bag.

10 Answer: No

Explanation: Samir surveyed 19.2 percent of the boys and 31.4 percent of the girls. He should increase the number of boys sampled or decrease the number of girls samples so the percentages are close to equal.

11 Answer: B

Explanation: Estimate the number of times with the product of 13 and 21.

12 Answer: A

Explanation: The number of words in the random sample with more than five letters is 111 out of 216 words. Divide 111 by 216 which is approximately 51%.

13 Answer: D

Explanation: The number of words in the random sample with 4 letters is 64 out of 256 words. Divide 64 by 256 which shows that 25% of the words have 4 letters.

14 Answer: Yellow

Explanation: According to the data, approximately 25% of the students surveyed prefer this color.

15 Answer: C

Explanation: Based on the data given in the table, over 50% of those surveyed were satisfied or very satisfied with their visit.

16 Answer: A

Explanation: Based on the data given in the table, the majority of those surveyed were satisfied or very satisfied.

17 Answer: A

Explanation: Based on the data given in the table, most of those survey (75%) were satisfied or very satisfied.

18 Answer: Approximately 150.

Explanation: According to the data, 16 people preferred green and 7 people preferred yellow out of 159 people surveyed. This is approximately 15% of the students.

19 Answer: B

Explanation: The number of each color of marble is based on the percentages given in the table.

20 Answer: No

Explanation: Answers may vary. The quantity of prime numbers will decrease as you near 1,000, because more of the larger numbers are multiples of the smaller and single digit numbers.

STATISTICS AND PROBABILITY: UNIT 2 - COMPARE AND INFER TWO POPULATIONS

1 Answer: C

Explanation: The mean is the sum of the values divided by the total number of values. Both means result from 301/5.

2 Answer: C

Explanation: The shape of the data shows most of Mrs. Moore's students are taller than Mr. Bell's students.

3 Answer: A

Explanation: The mode is the value occurring most often in a data set.

4 Answer: D

Explanation: The data values in Mrs. Lunchin's class start at 55 inches and ends at 62 inches. he data values in Ms. Ratliff's class start at 56 inches and ends at 62 inches.

5 Answer: B

Explanation: The median is the middle value when the data is in numerical order.

6 Answer: A

Explanation: The spread for Katrina's data is 5. The spread for Martin's data is 4. The difference between the two is 1.

7 Answer: C

Explanation: The most common height in Mr. Jackson's class is 60 inches. The most common height in Mr. Covinga's class is 59 inches.

8 Answer: 1, higher

Explanation: The median temperature is 17 degrees in Canton and the median temperature is 16 degrees in Milwaukee.

9 Answer: 5.6, 4.8

Explanation: Calculate the mean by adding the all of the values associated with the data points, then dividing the sum by the number of data points.

10 Answer: The center of the data from the semi-finals is $\frac{1}{2}$ point larger than the center of the data from the finals.

Explanation: Answers may vary. The data from the semi-finals is centered around $10\frac{3}{4}$ seconds. The data from the finals is centered around $10\frac{1}{2}$ seconds.

11 Answer: C

Explanation: The data shown in the table supports this inference. Three out of 5 fish weigh more than 20 ounces.

12 Answer: A

Explanation: The data shown in the table supports this inference. Lelita's shortest song is 3.75 minutes, and Yaminah's shortest song is 3.8 minutes.

13 Answer: C

Explanation: The range of Bryson's data is 4 hours. If the missing value is 5, then the range of Zane's data is greater than the range of Bryson's data.

14 Answer: B

Explanation: The average number of hours of sleep for each student in Mario's class is 2.73 hours greater than the average number of hours of sleep of each student in Gabriel's class.

15 Answer: D

Explanation: Find the missing values with these equations: $(102 + x)/5 = 26$ and $(75 + x)/5 = 23$. Compare the solutions.

16 Answer: A

Explanation: For the median value of Asha's bake time to be 20 minutes, the missing value is 20 minutes. For the median of Hattie's bake time to be 27 minutes, the missing value is 27 minutes.

17 Answer: A

Explanation: Based on the random sample, approximately 54% of the students ride the bus. Translating that (proportionally) to the entire school would mean approximately 1,100 students ride the bus.

18 Answer: 5

Explanation: Solve the equation $(60 + x)/8 = 8$. The missing value for Chapter 1 is 4. Solve the equation $(47 + x)/8 = 7$. The missing value for Chapter 2 is 9.

19 Answer: 11

Explanation: The missing value of the data set is 11. The range is the difference between the greatest and least values in a data set.

20 Answer: The mean height for both teams is 60.2 inches, although the data from the Falcons team has a larger spread.

Explanation: Answers may vary. Calculating the mean results in the same answer. The range (spread) of the data from the Ravens is 3 less than the range of the data from the Falcons.

STATISTICS AND PROBABILITY: UNIT 3 - PROBABILITY MODELS

1 Answer: B

Explanation: There are no black marbles in the bag, so the event is impossible.

2 Answer: A

Explanation: The probability of drawing a white marble is $\frac{1}{15}$, which is close to 0, or unlikely.

3 Answer: B

Explanation: The probability of drawing a red marble is $\frac{10}{14}$, which is 71%. This is a likely event.

4 Answer: 5/6

Explanation: The number cube has 5 numbers out of 6 numbers that are greater than 1.

5 Answer: $\frac{1}{2}$

Explanation: The prime numbers on the number cube are 2, 3, 5, 7, 11, and 13.

6 Answer: B

Explanation: The chance of landing on a 3 is $\frac{1}{6}$, so divide 450 by 6.

7 Answer: D

Explanation: The chances of landing on a 2 or 4 is $\frac{1}{3}$ or 33%. Thirty-three percent of 200 is approximately 67.

8 Answer: A

Explanation: The chances of someone selecting the color red is $\frac{8}{24}$ or $\frac{1}{3}$.

9 Answer: 32

Explanation: In his initial draws, $\frac{7}{13}$ straws are 2-inches long. Multiply $\frac{7}{13}$ times 60. The expected outcome of a selecting a 2-inch straw from a set of 60 straws is 32 out of 60.

10 Answer: $\frac{5}{8}$

Explanation: The experimental probability is 10 out of 16 or 10/16, or in simplest form, 5/8.

11 Answer: B

Explanation: Since the number spinner landed on "1" so many times, the probability of landing on "1" is greater than the figure shows. Either there are more "1s" on the actual wheel or the size of the "1s" space is larger than the figure shows.

12 Answer: A

Explanation: A standard dice contains 6 numbers, one of which is a 3. Therefore, the expected fraction of possible outcomes for rolling a 3 is $\frac{1}{6}$.

13 Answer: B

Explanation: The fraction 11/36 represents the possibility of rolling at least one five. There are 36 possible outcomes, or combinations. Out of those 36, 11 outcomes include at least one five. The fraction 11/40 is less than 11/36.

14 Answer: $\frac{1}{5}$

Explanation: In his original experiment, 5 out of 15 rolls show the pair of die have a sum of 7. This equates to a probability of 0.2 or $\frac{1}{5}$.

15 Answer: $\frac{3}{20}$

Explanation: The chance of selecting an "h" is 3 out of 20.

16 Answer: B

Explanation: In combinations, order of the event does not matter. If there are n objects and take r at a time, ${}_nC_r$ represents the number of combinations. Calculate a combination with $\frac{n!}{(n-r)!}$.

17 Answer: A

Explanation: The total number of possible outcomes can be determined by multiplying

6 × 6 × 2, using the Fundamental Counting Principle.

18 Answer: D

Explanation: The number of combinations of n things taken r at a time is written as C(n, r) or ${}_nC_r$.

19 Answer: 108

Explanation: Calculate the number of possible combinations by multiplying numbers in each category: $(3 \cdot 3 \cdot 3 \cdot 4) = 108$.

20 Answer: 180

Explanation: Calculate the number of possible combinations by multiplying numbers in each category: $(3 \cdot 4 \cdot 3 \cdot 5) = 180$.

STATISTICS AND PROBABILITY: CHAPTER REVIEW

1 Answer: A

Explanation: Counting the children in 10 random rows is a random sample in which all members of the group have an equal chance of being selected.

2 Answer: No

Explanation: There are three colors of marbles in the bag, not two.

3 Answer: Blue

Explanation: According to the data, approximately 4% of the students surveyed prefer blue. Thus one can conclude that approximately $\frac{1}{3}$ of the population prefers this color.

4 Answer: C

Explanation: The data shows that 25% of the students in Jada's class play basketball. Extending this projection to the entire school means approximately 50 students play basketball.

5 Answer: 17

Explanation: The data is clustered around the center value of the data set. The median is the center number.

6 Answer: D

Explanation: The range of a data set is the spread. The spread for Isabel's data is 5. The spread for Pedro's data is 4. The difference between the two is 1.

7 Answer: C

Explanation: The missing value for Group A is 1 or 4, and the missing value for Group B is 4.

8 Answer: C

Explanation: If the chances of drawing a red marble is unlikely, the number of red marbles is significantly lower than all of the other colors combine.

9 Answer: D

Explanation: The probability of drawing a black marble is $\frac{5}{10}$, which is 50%. This is an neither likely or unlikely event.

10 Answer: C

Explanation: The probability of drawing a white marble is 0%. This event is impossible because the bag contains no white marbles.

11 Answer: 8

Explanation: Determine the missing number in Chapter 1 with the equation $(51 + x)/9 = 7$ and in Chapter 2 with the equation $(68 + x)/9 = 8$. Find the difference between the two solutions.

12 Answer: C

Explanation: Since 23 out of 60 pencils selected were black, the bag contains approximately 38% black pencils. Multiply 150 by 0.38 to estimate the number of black pencils in the bag.

13 Answer: A

Explanation: The probability of selecting a blue pencil is 10%. If 10% of the pencils are blue, this means approximately 18 pencils are blue.

14 Answer: D

Explanation: The probability of selecting a red pencil is $\frac{15}{225}$ which simplifies to $\frac{1}{15}$.

15 Answer: C

Explanation: The probability model correctly represents the ratio of the number of times the event occurs, and the total number of equally likely possible outcomes.

16 Answer: A

Explanation: The probability model correctly represents the ratio of the number of times the event occurs, and the total number of equally likely possible outcomes.

17 Answer: B

Explanation: The probability model correctly represents the ratio of the number of times the event occurs, and the total number of equally likely possible outcomes.

18 Answer: B

Explanation: The probability of two specific independent events occurring is the product of their individual probabilities.

19 Answer: A

Explanation: Ordering fish or squash are independent events. Thus, the probability of the next person ordering fish and squash is the product of the probabilities. The probability of an individual ordering fish is $\frac{1}{2}$ and the probability of an individual ordering squash is $\frac{5}{14}$. Multiply those two probabilities.

20 Answer: C

Explanation: Each coin flip is an independent event, meaning the occurrence of one-coin flip does not affect the probability of the other event. There are 8 possible outcomes for flipping three coins.

STATISTICS AND PROBABILITY: EXTRA PRACTICE

1 Answer: No

Explanation: By ensuring a proportional amount of surveys were completed each day (20%) from each group, Paola attempts to collect valid data, but this type of survey obtains feedback mostly from the customers who feel very positive or very negative about their experience.

2 Answer: There is probably more dimes and pennies than nickels in the jar.

Explanation: Answers may vary. Based on the data, approximately 50% of the coins are dimes, 40% are nickels, and the remaining 10% are pennies.

3 Answer: 23

Explanation: The data shows approximately 42% of the monkeys are male.

4 Answer: No

Explanation: Answers may vary. The ratio of prime numbers to composite numbers will decrease as the numbers increase toward 100, because more of the larger numbers are multiples of the smaller/single digit numbers.

5 Answer: Spelling

Explanation: The range of scores on the spelling test is approximately 95 and the range of scores on the English test is approximately 53.

6 Answer: The data from the semi-finals is clustered in a different way than the data from the finals.

Explanation: Answers may vary. The data from the semi-finals is clustered in two areas; around 10 and 11 seconds. This is a bimodal distribution. The data from the finals is skewed to the right of $10\frac{1}{4}$ seconds.

7 Answer: The range of shoe sizes is the same. The median shoe size is 10 in sample A and 9 in sample B.

Explanation: Answers may vary. The range is the difference between the greatest and the least values in the data set. The median is the middle number in the data set when the numbers are ordered from least to greatest.

8 Answer: The range of shoe sizes is the same, indicating that both groups have a similar spread.

Explanation: Answers may vary. The median shoes size is 10.

9 Answer: 0

Explanation: The event is impossible. The number 1 is not a prime number.

10 Answer: $\frac{1}{3}$

Explanation: The probability of selecting an even number from the set of cards is $\frac{1}{3}$ because 4 out of 6 expressions result in an odd number.

11 Answer: 0

Explanation: There are no odd number cards in this set.

12 Answer: $\frac{1}{5}$

Explanation: The experimental probability is 3 out of 15 or 3/15, which In simplest form, is 1/5.

13 Answer: Yes

Explanation: If 7/10 of the first attendees are male, then the probability that an attendee is male is 70%.

14 Answer: $\frac{4}{9}$

Explanation: Answers may vary. Since the wheel lands on blue 8 out of 18 times, or 8/18, which reduces to 4/9.

15 Answer: 11 out of 36 or 11/36.

Explanation: There is a total of 36 products in the sample space, with 11 products greater than 15.

16 Answer: No

Explanation: The numbers 6 and 12 will appear on both number cubes, which means the chances of rolling these two numbers is greater than the other numbers.

17 Answer: No

Explanation: The number 2 will appear on both number cubes, which means the chances of rolling a 2 is twice as likely as rolling any other number.

18 Answer: 96

Explanation: The Fundamental Counting Principle states that the number of possible combinations is determined by multiplying the number of choices in each category: $(4 \cdot 4 \cdot 3 \cdot 2) = 96$.

19 Answer: 10/81

Explanation: The probability of selecting a consonant letter is 5/9, and the probability of selecting an "s" is 2/9. Since the questions asks for the probability of selecting a constant and then an "S", multiply the probabilities. They are independent events because the first draw is returned.

20 Answer: 1/10

Explanation: The probability of selecting a marble that is not green is 1/2, and the probability of selecting an orange marble,because the first marble was not replaced, is 3/15. Multiply the two probabilities because both events happen.

COMPREHENSIVE ASSESSMENTS
ASSESSMENT 1

1 Answer: Peaches

Explanation: The unit rate for apples is 2.85 ÷ 5 ($$0.57) and the unit rate for peaches is 3.5 ÷ 7 ($0.50).

2 Answer: Detergent B

Explanation: The unit rate for Detergent A is 4.99 ÷ 25 ($0.20) and the unit cost for Detergent B is 7.49 ÷ 90 ($0.08)

3 Answer: $y = 12x$

Explanation: He earns $12 for every hour so the relationship is $y = 12x$.

4 Answer: C

Explanation: Subtract 68 – 55 to find the difference. Then, divide the difference by the correct weight to find the percent error.

5 Answer: $12

Explanation: Subtract the original deposit from the current balance.

6 Answer: B

Explanation: Rewrite the expression as $-6+15+8+2$ then add or subtract from left to right.

7 Answer: A

Explanation: Because subtracting a negative is the same as adding a positive, the problem is adding opposites, which results in 0.

8 Answer: C

Explanation: The problem becomes $(-5)/6 \times (-18)/1$,which simplifies, after cross cancelling, to -5×-3.

9 Answer: A

Explanation: Combine numbers from left to right: $-2 - 6 = -8$; $-8 + 9 = 1$; and $1 - 7 = -6$

10 Answer: $14

Explanation: Subtract 96 – 82.

11 Answer: D

Explanation: The written expression can be translated as $\frac{2}{3}x - \frac{1}{2}x = \frac{1}{6}x$.

12 Answer: D

Explanation: A discount of 24.5% means the discounted price is 75.5% of the original cost.

13 Answer: $\frac{6}{7}x + \frac{18}{7}$

Explanation: Simplify the expression using the distributive property and combining like terms.

14 Answer: D

Explanation: Convert gallons to quarts by multiplying 12 × 4. Then multiply by $\frac{1}{2} \times \frac{1}{2}$ cups.

15 Answer: B

Explanation: The open symbol means the solution is all numbers greater than -12.

16 Answer: Yes

Explanation: Round 4,258 to the nearest 100 (4,200) and divide by 700.

17 Answer: D

Explanation: Multiply the length and width of the room by 2 since the scale is marked in $\frac{1}{2}$ inches. Then multiply each dimension by 4.75 to accommodate the scale.

18 Answer: B

Explanation: The sum of the lengths of any two sides of the triangle is greater than the length of the third side. This is only true if the lengths are 4 cm, 5 cm, and 3 cm.

19 Answer: 8 or 10

Explanation: The sum of the lengths of any two sides of the triangle is greater than the length of the third side. The length of the third leg could be 8 or 10 inches.

20 Answer: A

Explanation: An 8-sided prism is an octagonal prism. Slicing it parallel to the base would create an octagon.

21 Answer: No

Explanation: When slicing a cone, both shapes are possible cross sections, but if the slice passes through the base of the cone, the cross section is a parabola.

22 Answer: C

Explanation: calculate the length of the radius by dividing 19.5 by 2 (9.75 mm). Find the area of the watch face using this expression: (3.14)(9.75)(9.75).

23 Answer: 10.5625π

Explanation: The length of the radius of the large circle is 7 centimeters. The length of the radius of the small circle is (7 – 3.75) or 3.25 centimeters. Use the formula for the area of a circle.

24 Answer: 10

Explanation: The measure of Angle TSU is 30, which means x is 10.

25 Answer: 27

Explanation: Find x using the equation $2x + 5 + 6x - 3 = 90$. The solution is x is 11. Then, use the expression $2x + 5$ to find the answer.

26 Answer: D

Explanation: Use the area formula for a trapezoid: A = 0.5h(B + b). The area of the playground is 5,859 square ft.

27 Answer: 160

Explanation: The volume of the large cube is 1,280 cubic inches. The volume of the 2×2×2 cube is 8 cubic inches. Divide 1,280 by 8.

28 Answer: A

Explanation: The sample is the best representative of the town because it would interview people at a variety of locations.

29 Answer: Yes

Explanation: Mrs. Johnson's data is included in the overall school wide data and impacts the percentage of students who were successful on the state writing assessment.

30 Answer: C

Explanation: Approximately 56.7% of the students in Ms. Davis' class play volleyball or soccer. Extending this projection to the entire school means approximately 56.7% or 196 students play one of these sports.

31 Answer: 31

Explanation: The data shows approximately 38.7% (43 out of 111) of the flamingo are males. (43/111) x 80 is approximately 31.

32 Answer: C

Explanation: The median value is the middle value presented when the data is in numerical order. If a data set has an even number of elements, then the median is the average of the two middle values.

33 Answer: Mr. Field's

Explanation: The box plot data shows the range between the 1st and 3rd quartiles is larger in this data set. Mr.s Quame's IQR is 91 – 71, and Mr. Field's IQR is 93 – 72.

34 Answer: B

Explanation: The center of the data is the same for both tests. The average is identical.

35 Answer: the same as or equal to

Explanation: The difference between the greatest and least values in both samples is 5 days. Both data sets have the same spread.

36 Answer: A

Explanation: The probability of the event occurring is close to 1, which means it is likely to occur.

37 Answer: B

Explanation: If the probability of the event is 1, the event is certain to occur.

38 Answer: $\frac{1}{2}$

Explanation: The event is equally likely or unlikely to occur.

39 Answer: C

Explanation: The results of the first experiment do not affect the second experiment. The chances are 50%, and 50% of 80 is 40.

40 Answer: A

Explanation: The chances of both coins landing on heads is 25%. Extending the number of flips to 50 means the coins may land on heads approximately 13 times.

41 Answer: 4

Explanation: A 20% chance over a 7-day period means the probability of snow is for 1.4 days out of 7 days. Over a 21-day period, this chance increases to 4.2 or 4 days, by multiplying 1.4 by 3.

42 Answer: B

Explanation: The probability model represents the ratio of the number of times the event could occur and the total number of equally likely possible outcomes. There are 9 green marbles out of the 20 marbles.

43 Answer: D

Explanation: There are 5 white marbles out of the 30 marbles. The results are not even close to the theoretical probability of drawing a white marble repeatedly. Thus, a situation has to exist that makes the probabilities invalid.

44 Answer: C

Explanation: Drawing each slip of paper is a dependent event. The number of combinations of 7 movies selected 4 at a time is written as C(7,4) or 7C4.

45 Answer: 120

Explanation: Using the Fundamental Counting Principle, the number of possible arrangements is found by $5 \times 4 \times 3 \times 2 \times 1 = 120$.

COMPREHENSIVE ASSESSMENTS ASSESSMENT 2

1 Answer: 15,000

Explanation: If he falls 750 feet in 3 seconds, then he falls 250 feet per second. Multiply 250×60.

2 Answer: $\frac{1}{300} = \frac{x}{1050}$

Explanation: Write a proportion that shows the proportional relationship between gallons of paint and square feet of wall space. There is more than one proportion.

3 Answer: $\frac{3}{48} = \frac{x}{80}$

Explanation: Write a proportion that shows the proportional relationship between cups of flour and cookies. There is more than one proportion.

4 Answer: B

Explanation: Multiply 360×1.15.

5 Answer: 11

Explanation: Solve this proportion or an equivalent proportion: $48/4 = 132/x$.

6 Answer: 14,787

Explanation: Calculate $14505 - (-282)$ or $14505 + 282$.

7 Answer: 7

Explanation: Add $15 + 9$.

8 Answer: D

Explanation: Divide -450 by 5. The value is negative because it is a loss of money.

9 Answer: $\frac{1}{2}$

Explanation: Multiply sion could be represented as $-\frac{2}{1} \times \frac{-3}{8} \times \frac{4}{6}$. The product is $\frac{3}{6}$, which simplifies to $\frac{1}{2}$.

10 Answer: 160

Explanation: Subtract $52000 - 48000$. Then, divide by 25.

11 Answer: (2+5n)/(3n+5)

Explanation: The verbal expression "the sum of ..." indicates a grouping. The word "quotient" means divide.

12 Answer: No

Explanation: Kina's first step is incorrect. Distribution does not simplify terms inside a parenthesis. Then she uses the correct steps for simplifying an expression involving distribution and like terms.

13 Answer: C

Explanation: Each side of an equilateral triangle has the same length. Multiply the side length by 3: $3(\frac{2}{3}x + \frac{1}{6})$ and simplify: $2x + \frac{1}{2}$.

14 Answer: C

Explanation: Ten gallons is 40 quarts. Multiply $\frac{1}{4}$ by 40.

15 Answer: 9 or 10

Explanation: Each page has an area of 240 square inches. Each picture is 24 square inches. Dividing 240 by 24 is 10. If she does not want to turn the pictures, then 9 pictures will fit on the page.

16 Answer: B

Explanation: The distance between the bed and dresser can be calculated with this proportion:
(0.5 in)/(4.75 ft) = (1.25 in)/x
Cross multiplying gives the expression in choice B.

17 Answer: Multiply the height of the model by 20

Explanation: Use this proportion to determine the height of the building:
$\frac{1}{20} = \frac{14\,3/8}{x}$
The actual height of the building, x, is 287.5 feet.

18 Answer: Set C

Explanation: In a triangle, the sum of the lengths of the two shorter sides must be more than the length of the longest side.

19 Answer: Set B

Explanation: In a triangle, the sum of the lengths of the two shorter sides must be more than the length of the longest side.

20 Answer: A

Explanation: A 12-sided prism is a dodecagon. Slicing it perpendicular to the base would create a shape which matches it's rectangular faces.

21 Answer: Yes

Explanation: The shape he creates is a rectangle with the same height as the solid, with a length equal to the length of the diagonal.

22 Answer: B

Explanation: The formula of the circumference is π (estimated as 3.14) times the length of the diameter.

23 Answer: Yes

Explanation: Divide 17 by 9. The diameter of the web camera is 1.89 inches.

24 Answer: 39

Explanation: Write the equation $4x + 3 + 4x - 9 = 90$. The solution is $x = 12$. Use the value of x in the expression $4x - 9$ to find the answer.

25 Answer: a = 148
b = 77

Explanation: Find a using supplementary angles (180 − 32). Use complementary angles to identify an angle with a measure of 58 degrees. Then, find b by subtracting the known angles from 180 (180 − 45 − 58).

26 Answer: 432

Explanation: The volume of 144 blocks is 144 × 3 × 3 × 3 = 3,888 cubic inches. Since 3,888 is $\frac{3}{4}$ of the volume of the toy box, the volume of the box must 5,184. Find the area of the base y dividing 5,184 by 12, which is 432 square inches.

27 Answer: B

Explanation: Calculate the surface area of the triangular prism using the area of the 2 triangular bases (70 sq cm each) and the area of the 3 rectangular faces (2 of them with an area of 192 sq cm and one with an area of 224 sq cm).

28 Answer: D

Explanation: Five-eighths of the sample size is approximately 62%.

29 Answer: No

Explanation: Melissa's sample may not be representative of the entire population because it is a convenience sample, and the sample size is small.

30 Answer: A

Explanation: Approximately 6.6% of the students in Bryson's grade plays hockey. Extending this projection to the entire school (575 × 6.6%) means approximately 38 students play hockey.

31 Answer: 31

Explanation: The data shows approximately 38.7% of the flamingo are males. Multiply 80 × 38.7%.

32 Answer: D

Explanation: The spread of both dot plots starts at 400 lbs and ends at 525 lbs.

33 Answer: Math Test

Explanation: The median in this data set is approximately 93%, while the median in the science data is set is approximately 85%.

34 Answer: D

Explanation: The lowest number of sick days listed for Group B is 2.

35 Answer: less than

Explanation: The mean for Sample A is 1.17 days, and the man for Sample B is 1.5 days.

36 Answer: B

Explanation: The probability of at least 1 coin landing on tails is 8/9. This means the event is likely.

37 Answer: 1/12

Explanation: One card has a 3 on it. The chance of drawing a 3 is $\frac{1}{12}$.

38 Answer: 10/12
or
5/6

Explanation: Ten cards have numbers greater than 2. The chance of drawing a number greater than 2 is $\frac{10}{12}$.

39 Answer: D

Explanation: Since 14 out of 50 marbles are yellow, the experimental probability is 14/50 or 7/25.

40 Answer: 30

Explanation: A 30% chance over a 30-day period means the probability of rain is 10 days out of 30 days. Over a 90-day period, the predicted number of rainy days increases to 30.

41 Answer: 6.3

Explanation: The chance of rain or snow is 45% chance over a 7-day period means it will rain or snow 3.15 days out of 7 days. This probability is extended to 6.3 days out of 14 days.

42 Answer: C

Explanation: The sample set represents 24 students, with 10 of the students being girls. This means that 14 of the students are boys.

43 Answer: 12

Explanation: For each person, the frequency with which a white cube is selected from the bag is 4 out of 10 times, which is a probability of 2/5 or 40%. If this probability is extended to the entire bag of cubes, approximately 12 cubes are be white.

44 Answer: B

Explanation: Using the Fundamental Counting Principle, the number of permutations are $5 \times 4 \times 3 \times 2 \times 1 = 120$

45 Answer: 3/25
or
12%

Explanation: Each event is independent. The probability of selecting a blue marble is 1/5, and the probability of selecting a green marble is 3/5. Multiply the two probabilities.

Made in the USA
Middletown, DE
07 December 2018